"Just what the hell do you think you're doing?" he asked.

It wasn't her imagination, Reanna realized. Although his voice vibrated with fury, it was the same low, husky drawl she remembered so clearly. It was him! Good Lord, it was really him! Her heart pounded with anxiety. *The man beside her, the man who had fathered her child, was Travis Martin!* Suddenly, she started to laugh.

"I'm glad you think it's so funny," he muttered, shoving her through the door with so much force that it reverberated on its hinges. "You won't be laughing in a few minutes."

Reanna rubbed her wrist where Travis's fingers had dug into her tender flesh. She had fallen off a horse, had met the man to whom she had blithely given her virginity five years ago, and had been manhandled by him, all within the space of ten minutes . . .

Jan Mathews

Although she grew up on a farm in a small southern Illinois town and has lived in Chicago for over twenty-five years, Jan Mathews was born in Kentucky and still calls it home. She is a wife, mother, registered nurse, and writer—sometimes in that order. With a son who has a rock band and two other children who are involved in a variety of activities, she is always busy. If she could have one wish in life it would be forty-eight-hour days. She swears that her family, as well as every volunteer organization known to man, senses that she is a soft touch. She has been active in Scouting, athletic clubs, and in the PTA.

Jan's idea of heaven would be to spend a week in the wilderness—minus poison ivy —camping and backpacking. She would love to raft the Chattooga, see the Grand Canyon on horseback, and watch Monday Night Football without being interrupted.

Dear Reader:

This month we're publishing memorable romances by two award-winning authors. Jan Mathews, a longtime favorite Second Chance at Love author, has earned honors from Waldenbooks, *Romantic Times, Affaire de Coeur,* and Romance Writers of America. And Jamisan Whitney, who made a critically acclaimed debut in category romance with *Driven to Distraction* (#315), is also the very first winner of the *Romantic Times* WISH (Women in Search of a Hero) award.

In her tenth Second Chance at Love novel, Jan Mathews offers a story charged with drama and passion. *Stranger From the Past* (#422) is a six-hanky read, a classic of the genre with a larger-than-life, commanding hero and a heroine whose poignant past will enlist your sympathetic identification. Spunky Reanna Williamson re-encounters the man who fathered her child in a reckless night of passion five years earlier, and discovers he's wealthy racehorse breeder Travis Martin—whose opulent estate she's been living on as an employee. Travis and Reanna make a marriage of convenience for the sake of their son, but their union ultimately becomes an utterly satisfying love match. There's special appeal here for readers who favor lifestyles of the rich and famous, and for horseracing fans and other horse lovers.

For readers who seek lightness and laughter, Jamisan Whitney displays her trademark breezy humor in her second Second Chance at Love novel, *Heaven Sent* (#423). Owners of rival bicycle messenger services, Bree Jeffries and Sam Leong meet when their bikes collide and they're thrown together in the back of a fortune-cookie truck! The comedy is punctuated by emotional moments as wary Bree learns to trust daredevil playboy Sam, even as Sam learns that life holds deeper satisfactions than the mere thrill of adventure. Not since the smash-hit movie *Breaking Away* has biking served as the backdrop for such a thoroughly engaging story. And, in keeping with the Second Chance at Love tradition of portraying characters from diverse cultural and ethnic backgrounds, *Heaven Sent* has a Chinese-American hero, and a half-Chinese, half-British heroine who was adopted from an orphanage by an American couple. So, although you certainly don't have to be of Asian extraction or an adoptee to enjoy *Heaven Sent,* this romance may be especially interesting to such readers, as well as to adoptive parents of Asian children.

Our other Berkley releases will offer you many additional hours of enthralling reading this September. In the novel *A Perfect Love* by Patricia Gallagher, set in the early 1960's, Carol and Jeffrey Courtland's Camelot-like marriage is dramatically put to the test when his child from a wartime liaison comes to live with them. From the grand dame of romance, Barbara Cartland, we have her latest Camfield novel, *The Earl Escapes,* and from the inimitable Georgette Heyer, another classic Regency Romance, *Arabella.* Award-winning Regency author Elizabeth Mansfield has a new release, *The Magnificent Masquerade,* while Cassie Edwards is launching a new series of sensual Indian romances with *Savage Surrender,* which *Romantic Times* has called "her best yet." And for fans of romances set in biblical times, best-selling author Roberta Gellis tells a fascinating tale of passionate love between a captive beauty and her keeper during the reign of King David in *Fires of Winter.*

Until next month, happy reading!

With best wishes,

Sincerely,

Joan Marlow

Joan Marlow
Editor, SECOND CHANCE AT LOVE
The Berkley Publishing Group
200 Madison Avenue
New York, New York 10016

SECOND CHANCE AT LOVE™

JAN MATHEWS
STRANGER FROM THE PAST

BERKLEY BOOKS, NEW YORK

STRANGER FROM THE PAST

Copyright © 1987 by Jan Milella

First edition published September 1987

ISBN: 0-425-10517-2

"Second Chance at Love" and the butterfly emblem are trademarks belonging to Jove Publications, Inc. The name "BERKLEY" and the "B" logo are trademarks belonging to Berkley Publishing Corporation.

Second Chance at Love books are published by
The Berkley Publishing Group
200 Madison Avenue, New York, NY 10016

Printed in the United States of America

10 9 8 7 6 5 4 3 2 1

To Lettie, for believing!

CHAPTER ONE

"HEY, MOM! LOOK!" ANDY REELED in a fish and swung around to show off his catch. At four years old, he was a typical boy—imaginative, mischievous, and uncoordinated.

"Andy, watch out!" Reanna shouted, knowing instinctively what was about to happen next. She hid her amusement as the squirming fish landed smack in Jennifer Martin's pert blond curls. Predictably, six-year-old Jennifer reacted with less than enthusiasm, and promptly threw a clod of mud at Andy. Before Reanna could reach them, a full-scale battle ensued.

"Hey kids! That's quite enough!" Reanna admonished, pulling the youngsters apart. She dropped the fish in Andy's pail and picked a fish scale from Jenny's hair. The past month she'd worked here at Martin Oaks tutoring Jonathan Martin's learning-disabled daughter had been a satisfying—as well as lively and enlightening—experience. Not only was she Jennifer's teacher, but Reanna had formed a close bond with Jennifer as well, voluntarily taking over the responsibility of the motherless child's daily activities. In an effort to entertain and yet provide learning experiences for both the girl and her own son, Reanna arranged daily outings. Obviously, fishing wasn't one of her better choices.

"Just look at you two," she said sternly, trying hard not to laugh. They were both spattered with mud, and resembled creatures from a science-fiction movie. "When Mrs.

1

Mackey sees you, she'll skin you both alive."

"*She* did it!" Andy pointed to Jennifer. "She threw dirt at me!"

"No, *he* did! He dropped that fish on me on purpose."

"My, my, what have you two been wallowing in?" Jennifer's grandfather called out. A thin, wiry man with a thick shock of gray hair, he walked with a cane, and hobbled to the pond, stifling a grin.

"Look, Gramps! Look what I caught!" Andy showed off his fish again. Although Mr. Martin wasn't really his grandfather, Andy had slipped into the habit of calling him Gramps, just like Jennifer. Though Reanna normally insisted Andy use formality with adults, she had let this one go. It made them all happy.

"That's the best kind of fish you can catch, Andy. It's special. It can do tricks," Mr. Martin said, chuckling out loud now.

"You sure?" Andy sounded doubtful, but his eyes grew round with expectation.

"Absolutely." The old man nodded gravely. "Do you want to see?"

When Reanna had first come to the farm, Mr. Martin wouldn't have bothered to chuckle over a child's exuberant antics. He'd been a crotchety old man who had little or no patience with children, even his own granddaughter. Ignoring his sharp tongue, Reanna had coerced him with a combination of psychology and cunning to participate in the children's daily activities and to accompany her on their outings. Now he looked forward to them with an almost adolescent zeal. And his arthritis had miraculously lessened.

"Watch the fins," he said, grasping the fish near the gills. It was a small catfish, and reacting physiologically, the sharp, spiny fins raised in protection.

"Wow!" Andy said.

"Wow, yourself." Reanna gathered their gear and started up the bank. "It's lunchtime, and you both need a bath."

"I'll take them in," Mr. Martin volunteered. "David mentioned this morning that you wanted to see Iron Scimitar. Why don't you slip down to the pasture now, while the children eat?"

Iron Scimitar was the newest Thoroughbred colt at Martin Oaks. Travis, the eldest of Mr. Martin's three sons, had recently purchased the horse and shipped it home. The entire Martin family had high hopes that the colt would be the next Triple Crown winner, and for the past week Reanna had tried to find time to inspect the horse for herself.

"David's busy right now, but Scimitar's grazing in the south pasture," Mr. Martin directed.

It didn't take Reanna long to find the horse. She leaned on the top rail of the fence and stared at him with admiration. He just might make the Martin dream a reality, she thought. His conformation was excellent: a clean, broad head with bright eyes; a sturdy, well-sloped shoulder; a deep chest and girth; a short, strong back; good, straight hind legs; and well-balanced quarters delineated by long, powerful muscles. His ears pricked forward alertly.

Her experienced eye for horseflesh told Reanna that this sleek steel-gray colt was fast, and yet had the stamina to endure long distances, a vital necessity in any great racehorse. She ducked under the fence and approached him quietly. He was well mannered for a two-year-old horse, she decided as she stroked his neck.

Although a quiver coursed through him, the horse stood immobile, merely switching his tail. He seemed big for his age, too, already standing about sixteen hands high. His withers struck Reanna just above her shoulder. She spoke soothingly and ran a hand down his forelegs, judging his soundness. He nuzzled her playfully, quite unlike the high-strung racehorse she had anticipated.

"Easy now," she murmured while she stroked his soft muzzle. The delicate nostrils flared, and he blew through his nose. Suddenly, unbidden memories flooded into Reanna's mind. Thoughts of her father, and of another colt —a big, lanky racehorse called Bold Intruder—seared her consciousness. For a second, the image was so real she was back in Florida, racing the horse across dew-covered meadows in the early mornings.

Reanna closed her eyes tight in a futile attempt to combat the pain of that recollection. She'd been a young, carefree girl then, working with her father training Thoroughbreds and attending school to obtain her baccalaureate degree. It had been a wonderful time of her life, a busy time, filled with love and hard work. But she hadn't seen her father or Bold Intruder in four years, and she wasn't likely to see either of them ever again. They were part of her past, part of the life she'd left behind when she'd fled to Kentucky, alone, afraid, and pregnant.

While she continued to stroke the horse, Reanna stared across the dark, rolling meadow of bluegrass that stretched beyond her. It was here, in this gentle atmosphere, that she'd healed, that she'd started a new life for herself and her son. But she hadn't forgotten. Even now, when the memory should have faded, she couldn't forget the man who was the father of her child. She'd met him at a party nearly five years ago, but his dark, saturnine features were indelibly imprinted on her mind, a constant, painful memory always waiting to taunt her...

It had all started on a sultry Florida evening. The night she graduated from college she attended a party with her friend, Shelly Robbins. Reanna knew some of Shelly's other friends were a bit wild, but the party turned out to be even wilder than her most outrageous imaginings.

She realized she was in over her head as soon as she

walked in the door. The living room was brightly lit and loud music blared from a stereo. The rest of the house was shadowed mysteriously. People were crowded all over the place, spilling from the rooms onto the pool area. She surveyed the couples entwined on the dance floor, and other couples, on sofas and in dark corners, doing more than dancing. She was certain the smoky haze in the room was from more than just ordinary cigarettes. The whole scene was way out of her league.

"Shelly," she whispered, "I think we should leave. This isn't our kind of party."

"Don't be silly," the other girl retorted. "This is going to be fun. Just look at all the gorgeous men."

"Shelly, we don't know anyone," Reanna pointed out.

"So we'll make new friends. Anyhow, in racing circles there's no such thing as a stranger. Look, there's Jack Carter." Shelly indicated the son of a neighboring horse owner. "If he can be here, so can we."

"It's not Jack Carter I'm concerned about," Reanna persisted. "It's us. Racing circles or not, this isn't our type of crowd."

"Look, Reanna, this isn't the Middle Ages. Why don't you stop being such a puritan and start acting sophisticated for a change? What's wrong with having a little fun?"

"Smoking pot is not sophisticated," Reanna said. "And neither is fending off advances from some drunk!" She glared angrily at a tall blond man who had walked by and pinched her bottom.

"So leave." Shelly winked at the man as she spoke. "Have fun walking home. I'm staying, and I intend to have a good time."

Reanna sighed impatiently. Leaving wasn't as easy as Shelly so flippantly implied. They'd driven over sixty miles from Ocala to Tampa in Shelly's car to visit a friend of a friend. "Shelly—"

"Come on, Reanna, this is a party, for godsake. What did you expect, milk and cookies? No one's doing anything wrong. The way you're acting you'd think someone was about to steal your virginity."

Reanna's virtue was one of Shelly's constant taunts. It was silly, but she was beginning to feel a bit guilty about having made it through college untouched. From the talk around campus, extolling the wonders of sex, she was an unfortunate minority, and, according to Shelly, downright freakish.

Shelly shoved a drink in her hand. "Here, maybe this will loosen you up."

Reanna eyed the glass warily. She wasn't accustomed to drinking. Aside from her father's disapproval of alcohol, she'd only recently turned twenty-one. "What is it?"

"It's champagne punch, what else? Just drink it and stop being such an almighty pain. Honestly, Reanna, I don't know why you bothered to come along. You should have stayed home with your dumb horses."

Shelly turned away and started across the room toward a man. Reanna stared after her, feeling foolish and naive. She didn't know why she'd come, either. She sighed again and looked at the punch. Anything that had strawberries in it had to be fairly innocuous, she reassured herself as she took a long swallow. It was fizzy, like cola, and she couldn't taste the champagne. It was good, too, cool and refreshing in the heat of the crowded room. She drank it quickly and refilled her glass.

For the next hour, Reanna sat near the punch bowl and studied the people milling around the room. Looking for tiny identifying characteristics or idiosyncrasies was a favorite pastime of hers. She supposed it stemmed from years of judging the qualities of horses, but she liked to memorize features and categorize people. Later, she could

easily recall their faces; their images were perfectly imprinted in her mind.

One woman kept fidgeting with her hair, wrapping a
single strand around and around a finger and letting it go,
only to repeat the gesture whenever she started to talk. The
man she was with had bushy eyebrows that flitted up and
down, narrowed and widened as he conversed.

Reanna's attention strayed to a man across the room.
There was something about him that intrigued her, though
at first glance his features weren't remarkable—a strong,
square jaw, an aquiline nose, and thick dark hair that tumbled over his forehead in disarray. She imagined he raked a
hand through it constantly in an impatient or unconscious
gesture. Moments later, she smiled when he confirmed her
observation, lifting his hand and running it through his hair
as he spoke to a group of men.

Reanna refilled her glass and continued to study him.
He was tall, at least a head taller than the other men in the
room, and he had a broad chest and shoulders that tapered
to narrow hips. He seemed older than the rest of the crowd,
perhaps in his late twenties. His face was tanned, as though
he spent a great deal of time outdoors.

Although his rugged features were attractive, there was
also something more, something that she sensed that set
him apart. A certain magnetism perhaps, an aura of energy,
or of command, and a sensuality, too, that probably drove
women wild. She liked the way he moved—smooth, lithe,
no wasted motions.

In a way, he reminded her of John Wayne. She couldn't
explain exactly why, for he didn't resemble the late actor
physically, except for his height. He *was* tall, and under the
casual slacks and open-necked shirt he was wearing he
looked lean and tightly muscled. The more she studied
him, the more he reminded her of the Duke.

She watched him while she sipped at another glass of

punch. It was really delicious, but it made her hungry. There were tiny butterflies dancing in her stomach. It had been foolish to skip dinner.

"Hell-o, baby," a man said, sitting next to her at the bar. "My horoscope said I was going to meet a hot chick in a red dress tonight. How's about you and me making Venus happy?"

Reanna was wearing a red silk sheath she'd borrowed from Shelly. It draped over her soft curves, dipping low in front, and was slit a few inches from the knee on both sides, baring the smooth expanse of her long legs. Since her normal attire was jeans and riding boots and a serviceable shirt, she'd felt alluring in the dress, until now.

She flicked her long blond hair over her shoulder, picked up her drink, and moved away. If she'd heard that tired cliché once, she'd heard it a thousand times. She started to find Shelly but was swept up in another man's arms. She whirled around the room with him, cringing as he stumbled over her toes.

Finally escaping, she withdrew to a corner and chatted with a group of men discussing horses. They were trainers, she discovered, and had just finished the season at Florida Downs. One of them was working with a two-year-old filly who had clocked five furlongs in 58.9 seconds, phenomenal time. Back in her element, Reanna felt herself relax.

After two more glasses of punch, she couldn't understand why she'd been so tense earlier. Shelly was right—she'd been acting silly. No one was doing anything wrong. In fact, everyone was having a wonderful time. The room had taken on a surrealistic glow; the haze resembled white, fluffy clouds, and the music was soft and enchanting. She tapped her foot to the beat. It would be nice to dance again —if she could find a partner who didn't trample her feet. She turned, intending to look for Jack Carter, when she noticed the Duke was sitting on a sofa, alone.

He was staring into the dark liquid in his glass, but he appeared to be concentrating on something else, something far away and terribly important. Earlier, when he'd danced with Shelly, he'd seemed preoccupied. He'd hardly noticed his partner, and Reanna couldn't imagine anyone not noticing Shelly. Suddenly, she decided to tell him he reminded her of John Wayne.

Maneuvering her way across the room proved to be a difficult task. Reanna was dizzy, probably from the heat or hunger, and people kept bumping into her. By the time she reached the attractive stranger, the room was spinning. She'd meant to plop on the sofa beside him but missed, and ended up on his lap. The expression on his face made her giggle.

"Pardon me," she said. "I can't understand why I'm so clumsy."

"Perhaps it's because you're drunk."

His smile was one of faint amusement. His voice was low and naturally husky. He spoke with a soft drawl, but Reanna couldn't for the life of her place the exact geographic region. She frowned at his remark.

"Oh, no, that's not possible. I don't drink." She held up her glass. "This is punch."

With a slight quirk of his eyebrow he tipped his glass to hers and drained the liquid. "Well, this is whiskey, and I'm making a concentrated effort to get smashed."

Reanna thought that was so funny she giggled again. Goodness, she hadn't giggled this much since she was in eighth grade and Johnny Timms shot spit wads at the teacher whenever the woman's back was turned. They stuck in her hair like tiny wads of cotton. "Are you?"

"Are I what?"

"Smashed."

"I think so," he said, frowning as though he wasn't certain. "I hope so, although it doesn't solve anything and I'll probably regret it in the morning."

"You'll have a headache," she told him, reaching up to sweep the lock of hair from his forehead. In an impulsive gesture, she traced her finger along his jaw and across to his lips. Then, unable to imagine what was making her so bold, she kissed him. It was a light, friendly kiss that lasted only seconds. "I wanted to meet you."

He narrowed his eyes and looked at her for a long time. It was as though he was just now seeing her. "So I gathered. Do you always introduce yourself with such abandon?"

"Oh, no." She started to laugh. She felt so wonderful. This party was fun. "It just seemed to be a good idea with you."

"You know," he said, putting down his empty glass and sliding his arms around her, "little girls like you shouldn't be out after dark. It's dangerous."

Reanna beamed at him. At five-eight, she had towered over all the boys until she'd reached high school. She couldn't remember anyone ever calling her "little." He had so much insight. "Will you protect me from the big bad wolf?"

"Sweetheart," he drawled, "I *am* the big bad wolf."

That was funny, too, Reanna decided, and laughed. He had quite a sense of humor. Everyone knew John Wayne was the safest man on earth. Why, she'd trust her life to him. He was the hero. "Nope." She shook her head firmly. "That's not true. You're the Duke."

He tilted his head and gave her a long, measured look. "I'm not familiar with the game, but I'll play anyhow. Is that who you want me to be?"

Reanna shook her head again. "No, silly, that's who you *are*."

"And who are you tonight?" he asked.

"My name's Reanna." She drew out the syllables, pronouncing it phonetically. "And I know, it's an unusual name."

"Well, Reanna, I think you're smashed, too, and that could be even more dangerous than being out after dark."

"I am not drunk," she insisted. "I'm sober as a judge." She suddenly decided the reason for her unconstrained behavior. "It's the strawberries," she declared. "They're magical. I've been eating magical strawberries, and I feel *wonderful*."

He arched an eyebrow at her. "Strawberries, huh?"

"Yes, and I'm having a marvelous time." She giggled and threw an arm around his neck. "You're so nice, Duke. I'm glad we met. Aren't you glad we met?"

"Sweetheart, I'm *delighted* we met." He started to gently massage her back. It felt so good she arched against him. "I'm just having a hell of a time believing it."

Reanna laughed. He was so different from any of the other men she'd met. He was funny and nice and not at all presumptuous. It seemed perfectly natural to put aside her drink and unbutton his shirt to see if he had hair on his chest like John Wayne. But she had to concentrate on each button. Her fingers kept fumbling.

"And I sure hope you know what you're doing," he said, staring at her with an odd expression, "because you're playing with fire, sweetheart, and you're liable to get burned."

Something flared in his eyes, some alien emotion she didn't understand and that her befuddled mind couldn't decipher. But she ignored it.

"I know exactly what I'm doing," she said, smiling because she had managed, finally, to open his shirt.

"Exactly?"

"Exactly." She spread her hands in the dark mat of hair that curled across his chest, and giggled. She couldn't remember now if John Wayne had hair on his chest or not. No matter, he reminded her of the actor anyway.

"Since you know exactly what you're doing, I think I'll light the fuse," he mumbled, clasping her tighter and drawing her close.

At first Reanna thought that was a strange remark, but she couldn't figure out what it was that disturbed her. Then she forgot what he said as his warm breath tickled her neck. Tiny shivers wisped along her spine. She gave up trying to decipher his comment and snuggled against him, thinking how pleasant it was to feel his lips slide along her throat and across one bare shoulder.

"You're a very beautiful woman, Reanna." His lips continued to nuzzle her neck as he pulled her against him.

"Thank you," she murmured back, delighted. Except for her father, no one had ever told her she was pretty. How could she be, always dressed for riding horses? Now she was doubly grateful to Shelly, first for bringing her, and second, for loaning her the dress.

"Would you like to dance?"

"Hmmm?" she asked dreamily.

"Let's dance."

Reanna didn't care whether they danced or not. It felt so good here on the sofa next to him, but she went into his embrace and wrapped her arms around his neck.

They danced again to the next song and the next and the one after that. She drank some more punch, laughing and teasing him with the strawberries while he downed a cocktail. Then they danced some more, for how long she couldn't guess, but some time passed. He didn't talk much, but then, neither did she. Articulation was a problem, so she giggled a lot and clung to him, swaying to the music.

Somehow, she knew it was late; somehow she knew she was behaving oddly; and somehow, she knew her inability to think should concern her, except it didn't. All she was aware of was never wanting to leave the circle of his arms, of never wanting to move away from his hard, firm body.

When her breasts brushed against him, she could feel her nipples harden through the thin fabric of her clothing. A tremor of delight thrilled through her as he moved his hands down her sides, across her hips and back up her body in a slow, sensuous motion. The silky texture of her dress rubbing against her bare skin heightened the strange excitement of his touch.

"I'm hot," she declared through the mist of sensation throbbing deep inside. She leaned her head back and ran her fingers through her thick mass of blond hair, lifting it from her neck and letting it tumble back down. "Are you hot, Duke?"

"Sweetheart, I'm burning up," he murmured, kissing the soft curve of her breasts her movements had inadvertently exposed. She giggled and squirmed away.

"Is there somewhere we could go?" She meant to add "where it's cooler," but she was too tired to form the words.

"I'm certain we can find somewhere," he said, still pulling her along in time to the music. He led her through the house to a door. As they slipped inside the empty room his lips met hers in a soft yet demanding embrace, moving commandingly over her mouth.

Vaguely, she heard the lock click; vaguely, she realized they were in a bedroom, alone. Something else clicked, too, something deep inside the recesses of her mind. What was he doing? What was *she* doing?

But her confusion was momentary, and her hesitation, too, as his lips traced an erotic path along her throat, and down, across the curve of her breast. His breath, harsh against her skin, was a tantalizing force, making her heart begin to pound in a rapid, dizzying rhythm. A longing she'd never felt before spread through her in a heated glow.

Reanna didn't object when he removed her dress and placed her on the bed; she felt cooler without her clothing. She realized she was naked and his bare skin was pressing against her, but then the tempest reclaimed her as his lips began an assault on her senses.

His mouth was searing on her heated skin, doing things to her that she'd never experienced—delicious, delightful things that made her feel hot and shaky inside. The touch of his callused hands caressing her bare skin made her think surely a wildfire was raging inside her. Her entire body was consumed by a white-hot blaze, trapped in an inferno of longing.

She heard herself cry out with pleasure when the fire focused and intensified between her thighs. It hurt, but for only a moment. After the initial pain, the warm flood of feelings inundated her again. She arched against him, matching his rhythmic movements by intuition, innocent of knowledge yet driven by need.

"My God," he whispered hoarsely, "you're magnificent." His movements grew faster and faster until she felt ravaged by the fiery blaze. At last an exhilarating throbbing started deep inside her, pleasure spread through her languid limbs, and the fire banked and smoldered until there was just the dim glow of fulfillment.

"Those certainly were magical strawberries, sweetheart."

Reanna heard his soft murmur, but she was so dizzy and overcome by fatigue that she couldn't comprehend what he was saying. Her limbs felt leaden, her mind bedazzled. She didn't want to move; she didn't want to think. She curled in his arms and closed her eyes, thinking only how cool and soothing his hand felt on her forehead, gently sweeping back her hair. The last thing she remembered before she fell asleep was his tender kiss.

* * *

A sharp feeling of nausea woke Reanna. At first she didn't know where she was. The harsh light hurt her eyes as she looked around the room, trying to orient herself. Her tongue felt thick and fuzzy and her head pounded. She half raised on the bed, her eyes widening in horror when she saw the naked man sprawled beside her. When she realized what she'd done, a sick, hollow feeling clutched at her stomach.

Quickly, she dressed and stumbled from the room, looking for Shelly. In the living room, people were sprawled all over. The stereo still blared. Her friend was curled in a chair, asleep. Reanna glanced at the clock and shook Shelly awake.

"Let's go," she whispered. All she wanted to do was run and hide, but Shelly was in no condition even to walk. Reanna half carried, half prodded her to the car. By the time she drove home to Ocala, the gray mist of dawn lit the sky. In less than an hour, her father would be up to exercise the horses.

After using the side of the road to be sick, Shelly was wide awake. Reanna continued to drive the car. Neither spoke about the party; they were both too concerned about getting inside before their families woke up. Since Reanna's father had worked for Shelly's father for several years, training and saddling his horses for races all over the States, they lived in a house provided by Glenn Robbins. It was small but cozy, and was located near the stables. She slipped quietly inside.

It seemed as though she had just fallen asleep when she heard the soft knock at her bedroom door. She knew it was her father. For ten years, ever since her mother died, they'd started the morning together. Today was no exception. She dragged herself from the bed and slipped on a robe.

Les Williamson was a tall, large-boned man with sandy hair that was rapidly thinning as he approached sixty. Reanna had been born late in his life, when he'd least expected a child, but he'd always been there for her, even when the thought of raising a daughter alone confounded him. He was a soft-spoken man with high ideals and a strict moral code. Reanna knew that if he ever discovered what she'd done, he'd be devastated.

He took one look at her and frowned. She was surprised to watch him stifle a grin. "You look like you could use some coffee," he said after a moment.

Reanna forced a tight smile and nodded. She followed him into the kitchen and eased into a chair. "My head hurts."

"I can imagine." He puttered around the kitchen making coffee, being careful not to bang anything or make loud noises. "How much did you drink?"

Just the thought of alcohol made her stomach start to roil again. She flinched as a cup fell to the floor. "Too much. I know this sounds stupid, but I didn't realize champagne punch could be so devastating."

Her father laughed, picking up the broken pieces and giving her an apologetic glance. "It can pack a wallop. The problem is, it tastes so good you drink too much. I'll never forget my first hangover," he went on. "It was bourbon, and I was sick for three days."

"I'd like to forget mine," Reanna mumbled. And everything else, too, she wanted to add.

"You were out late. Did you have a good time?"

She felt her face burn with shame. All her life, he'd protected her and tried to guide her. "I'm sorry if I woke you."

"You didn't wake me, sweetheart." He sat beside her and sipped his coffee thoughtfully while Reanna forced the gall from rising in her throat. *He* had called her sweetheart, too. "You know, Reanna," her father continued, "quite often that kind of experience can teach you more than all my lectures combined."

Reanna had to clench her teeth to keep from being sick. How true, she thought bitterly, how very true. Experience was the best teacher of all. Unfortunately, it was also a harsh mentor.

"The next time you'll know your limit," he said, chuckling again. "But it's a hell of a way to learn."

She simply nodded and sipped the scalding coffee, hoping it would calm her. They sat in silence for a while. Reanna was beginning to feel human again when her father covered her hand with his.

"Sweetheart, with all the confusion around here, the racing season at the Downs and your graduation, I haven't had a chance to tell you how proud I am of you. I know how hard you worked for your degree. Your mother would have been proud, too," he added, his voice thick with emotion.

Reanna was shocked to see tears glinting in his eyes. Les Williamson wasn't a demonstrative man, and emotional displays were uncharacteristic, but he had worshiped his wife. Don't say it! her mind screamed. Please don't say it!

"You've carried on her name, Reanna, and you're a tribute to her memory. All I have to do is look at you to remember what a fine woman your mother was."

"Oh, Daddy," she whispered, heartsick over what she'd done. When she started to cry, he folded her in his arms and patted her awkwardly. *I've been with a man, Daddy,* she wanted to shout. *I've been with a man and I don't even know his name!* She bit her lip in order to keep silent. She couldn't stand the thought of what it would do to him if he knew.

"Come on," he said when she'd regained control. "Let's

exercise the horses. You can ride Bold Intruder. Did I tell you Glenn is thinking of selling him? I've told him over and over that this colt is a natural-born winner, but he doesn't want to bother with him."

Bold Intruder had a bad habit of nipping other horses. It wasn't really malicious, but it caused quite a furor in the paddocks or in the starting gate. Sometimes, when he was among the first horses loaded into the starting gate, he would reach across and bite the ear of the horse beside him. He was like a big kid who hadn't grown up. They were thinking of using a special bit to remind him his behavior was unacceptable.

"It would be a mistake to sell him," Reanna said, forcing her mind to concentrate on the tasks that needed to be done. "Have you mentioned the bit?"

"No, I want to try it first. By the way, did you hear about the fire over at Lakeland?" Lakeland was a track located in south-central Florida. The racing season there had just gotten underway. "I hear they managed to rescue a few horses, but the Oaks stables lost most of its Thoroughbreds. They're still investigating the cause."

Fire was something all horsemen dreaded. When housing hundreds of valuable animals together, safety precautions were uppermost in everybody's mind. But despite the most stringent precautions and regulations, tragedy sometimes struck. "I guess we're fortunate you delayed shipping Intruder," she said.

"Yes, I count my blessings. It was a terrible tragedy."

Her father poured the rest of his coffee into the sink. "Reanna, you seem awfully upset over last night."

"Yes, I am," she admitted, turning away so he couldn't see the tears brimming in her eyes again.

"Honey, making one little mistake isn't the end of the world. So you drank too much. The value of an experience is learning from it and putting it behind you."

Those words were what sustained Reanna through the next three months. She kept repeating them over and over, through the fatigue, then the nausea that she blamed on a lingering case of stomach flu. Apparently, the chances of becoming pregnant on a first and only sexual encounter were phenomenally high. The doctor confirmed that fact with staggering figures, but he was amazed at her incredulity.

"A common misconception, my dear," he said, "under which many women eventually labor."

Reanna didn't miss the pun, but she was too overcome with shock for it to be funny. At first, after her pregnancy was confirmed, she inquired discreetly about the stranger at the party, then not so discreetly, and finally, frantically. But the host of the party didn't even remember her, let alone a tall, dark-haired man.

"I was more interested in the women, sweetie," he said when she telephoned. "Which one were you?"

Shelly didn't remember the man, either. "He reminded you of John Wayne but he didn't look like John Wayne. Come on, Reanna."

She described him over and over, hoping Shelly would remember something, anything that would help her find the father of her child. At the various tracks where they raced, she inquired about him, constantly searching the crowds, looking for those dark features. Reanna wasn't certain what she'd do if she found him. She hadn't thought that far ahead. All she wanted was a name to go with the face.

It took her two months to admit defeat, and even then, she didn't make plans other than to apply for a teaching position in the fall. She continued to work with her father, exercising and training horses. Miraculously, she kept her pregnancy a secret. By then, she was well into her sixth month. The morning she couldn't fit into her loosest pants, she decided it was time to tell her father. For as long as she lived, she would remember his reaction.

"You're *pregnant?*" he thundered, his face turning purple. "You're pregnant and you don't even know who the father is? My God, Reanna. How could you? How could you sully her name?"

"Daddy," she said, "please try to understand. It was a mistake. I made a mistake."

"Mistake? You're a disgrace to your mother's memory, and you tell me you made a mistake?"

"Daddy, please," she begged, unable to prevent tears from streaming down her face.

"I have to go," he said. He looked suddenly old; his shoulders were stooped in defeat, and fatigue lined his face. "I have to exercise the horses."

"I'll help," she offered eagerly, anxious to do anything to mend the rift.

"No!" he said sharply. "I don't want your help, not today. I can't look at you today and remember her."

"Daddy, please try to understand," she repeated when he opened the door to leave.

He turned and looked at her. It was as though she was seeing a stranger. There was repugnance in his gaze, along with disappointment and despair. "Don't call me that, Reanna." He choked on her name. "Don't call me 'Daddy.' As far as I'm concerned I don't have a daughter. Right now, I don't ever want to see you again."

Reanna was stunned. She knew he'd be angry and disappointed, but she hadn't expected hatred. She cried most of the morning. That afternoon, she packed a few personal items, took what money she had in the house, and left. She had one thing in common with Les Williamson, and that was a fierce, stubborn pride. She couldn't stay any longer. It was time to grow up.

At the bus station, she bought a ticket to Lexington,

Kentucky, because it was the same place the person in line in front of her was going. For three days, she stayed in a hotel, trying to plan her future. She was pregnant, and it was about time she faced that fact and sought medical attention. And she was alone in a strange city. The next day she entered the home for unwed mothers. The rest was simple. She bought a cheap wedding band, used "Mrs." instead of "Miss" to circumvent the morals clause in a teaching contract, and obtained a position at the Price School for Learning-Disabled Children.

For four years, she'd worked for Leona Price and struggled to support Andy. During the summers, she supplemented her meager income by working for area families. This year, on the recommendation of Miss Price, she was working with Jennifer Martin. Jennifer was one of those borderline children who would greatly benefit from intense personal instruction. In fact, the child was doing so well it was doubtful if she would have to return to special school this fall.

It was odd that she'd ended up at Martin Oaks, Reanna thought, in the midst of a racing family. It was like coming home. Jennifer was a delight, and aside from her teaching duties, Reanna had formed a friendship with the rest of the family. The talk of Thoroughbreds, tracks, and timing fascinated her, as always. Although he interfered a lot, and vocalized his opinion about everything, including the children, the elder Mr. Martin had in essence given up the reins of his estate to his sons. Of the three, David seemed to know the most about horses. Jonathan was happier with his paintings. Ever since his wife's death he'd buried himself in his art. The eldest, Travis, was in Saratoga Springs, buying stock. Reanna hadn't met him yet, but she was looking forward to it. According to David, Travis was the real horseman of the family.

The big gray colt stamped the ground impatiently and

nudged her, bringing her back to the present. Reanna stroked his sleek coat again. It had been years since she'd ridden, and he seemed so well trained. Before she realized what she was doing, she had grasped his mane and pulled herself astride. She would take him for a short run across the pasture, just for the sheer pleasure of feeling the wind in her hair. Nothing would happen, and they would both enjoy the run.

The horse responded instantly, streaking across the grass. Reanna clutched his mane, leaning low on his neck, and tucked her legs close to his sides. She felt as if she were part of him as he stretched out, his long, effortless strides gliding them across the wildflower-strewn meadow. And he was fast. For a moment, she was back in Florida, riding Bold Intruder. She forgot everything, including the fact that she was astride someone's valuable horse and possibly putting the animal in danger.

Then, as his muscles bunched beneath her, she glanced up and realized he was preparing to jump the fence. She pulled back on his mane, trying to stop him, but he was in full gallop and evidently determined, for he ignored her. His forelegs left the ground in a giant leap. She leaned low to help him make the jump, tightening her thighs and clenching her heels against him.

Reanna knew she was going to fall off. Staying astride a horse while jumping an obstacle was difficult. Going up was no problem, but coming down was another matter, and without a saddle and bridle it was an impossibility. It wasn't that she was afraid to fall. She'd tumbled from a horse many times and it was equivalent to falling from a tall chair. What concerned her was hanging on so she didn't tumble over his neck, and worse, hoping he could make the jump without shattering his forelegs.

The squeal of brakes came to her as though in a dream. A car flashed past just as they sailed over the fence. As the horse's feet came down, she felt herself slip. Within seconds, she was sitting on the dusty driveway. Without a rider, the horse slowed and circled, shaking his head as if he wondered what had happened to her. Reanna was grateful to see he wasn't limping or injured.

She picked herself up from the ground and dusted off her jeans, intending to apologize for frightening the man who was striding toward her, furious. She'd practically landed on top of his head.

Moments later, the words died on her lips. She felt the blood drain from her face as she stared at the features she had memorized so long ago. Her legs grew weak and lifeless. For a second, she thought she might start to laugh hysterically. Here, standing in front of her, was the man who had haunted her dreams for the past four years; here, standing in front of her, was the father of her child.

CHAPTER TWO

REANNA CLOSED HER EYES, as though to blot out his image. *It's not true,* she thought. *It's not possible!* Not after all these years; not after all she'd endured. Fate wouldn't be that cruel. It was a bad dream. It was her imagination playing tricks.

"Just what the hell do you think you're doing?" he asked.

It wasn't her imagination, Reanna realized. Although his voice vibrated with fury, it was the same low, husky drawl she remembered so clearly. It was him! Good Lord, it was really him! Her heart pounded with anxiety. She felt herself start to sway as a welcome void of blackness engulfed her.

It was his painful grip on her arm that brought Reanna back to reality. "You damned hippies!" he was shouting as he pushed her in front of him toward the house. "Or whatever it is you call yourselves. I've let you camp out on my land and tolerated your destruction, but I'll be damned if you'll touch my horses."

Through the haze in her mind, Reanna recalled Mr. Martin and Jonathan discussing the group of college students that was camping on the outer fringes of the estate. They called themselves "teepee children," and evidently this man thought *she* was one of them. But Reanna was too overcome with shock to correct his impression or to fight him. She let him propel her toward the house while her mind absorbed fragments of his remarks. He had called

Martin Oaks *his* land. His land? Just who was this man?

"Charlie!" he shouted to a groom who had come running toward them. "Get a bridle on Excalibur and take him to a stall. Now that he knows he can jump the fence, that damned horse will get every mare on the farm impregnated! And get David!"

Reanna blinked in confusion as they clambered up the steps to the stately mansion, his grip forcing her to walk at breakneck speed. Who was Excalibur? She'd been riding Iron Scimitar, or at least she'd thought she'd been riding Iron Scimitar. The irony of the situation struck her, and hysteria bubbled into her throat. It was the wrong horse! She'd been riding the wrong horse! *And the man beside her, the man who had fathered her child, was Travis Martin!* Suddenly, she started to laugh.

"I'm glad you think it's so funny," he muttered, shoving her through the door with so much force that it reverberated on its hinges. "You won't be laughing in a few minutes."

"Travis, what in the world is going on?" Jonathan skidded to a halt just inside the entryway. "What's happened? Is Jenny all right?"

David burst through the door behind them just as Mr. Martin rounded the corner. "My God, Travis, let her go," the older man ordered. "Can't you see you're hurting her?"

"You're damned right I'm hurting her," Travis retorted, pushing her toward the study. "She's lucky I haven't broken her neck. As far as I know, Jennifer's fine," he said to Jonathan, "but I just caught this woman sailing Excalibur over the fence. I'm calling the police. This time we're pressing charges."

"The police? You can't call the police!" Jonathan exclaimed. "You can't have her arrested."

"Watch me."

"Travis!" Mr. Martin said more firmly. "You're hurting Reanna. Let her go, now!"

They had all been talking at once; then, abruptly, the shouting ceased, and there was total silence. By now, Reanna had stopped laughing and was staring dispassionately at the three men. It was strange. Everything that was happening registered intellectually, but she felt oddly emotionless, as though she weren't really part of the situation.

Travis slowly released her. "Reanna?"

Somehow, despite the numbness that gripped her, she sensed his intense scrutiny and looked up at him. The features she remembered so well were a study in bewilderment. His eyebrows were furrowed in a dark slash across his forehead, and his steel-gray eyes were clouded with questions. The errant lock of hair had fallen across his forehead. He swept it back in the familiar, impatient gesture.

"This is Reanna Williamson, Jennifer's tutor for the summer," Mr. Martin said.

"Tutor?" Travis echoed.

"And this raving maniac is my son, Travis." The pride in the old man's voice belied his words. "Are you all right, my dear?"

Reanna nodded and rubbed her wrist where Travis's fingers had dug into her tender flesh. "Yes," she answered, "yes, I'm fine." But she wasn't fine; she was far from it. She had fallen off a horse, and met the man to whom she had blithely given her virginity five years ago, and had been manhandled by him, all within the space of ten minutes.

"My apologies for the misunderstanding." Travis still seemed confused. He kept staring at her and frowning. "You should have mentioned who you were."

Reanna was struck by the absurdity of his innocent remark. What should she have said? *Hi there! So sorry for taking your horse for a ride, but haven't we met before?* Or maybe: *Oh, hi, remember me? We spent the night together five years ago.*

"I'm sorry, too, for riding the horse," she finally murmured. "It was a foolish and irresponsible thing to do."

"Excalibur's a jumper." David spoke for the first time. He was thin and wiry like his father, but now Reanna noticed he had the same gray eyes as his brother. "We all knew it was a matter of time before he took that fence. Travis is just mad because Excalibur's his favorite riding horse. By the way, Charlie said you rode him bareback. Why didn't you tell us you were an experienced horsewoman?"

It took Reanna several moments to realize that David had asked her a question. She frowned, trying to force her mind to function. "It's been a long time since I've ridden," she finally managed to explain. "I guess I acted on impulse."

"Well, it's a good thing you found Excalibur instead of Scimitar." David turned to his brother. "Travis, Iron Scimitar is the meanest horse I've ever handled. He'd sooner kick you than look at you. I can't understand what you see in him."

Reanna remembered David telling her a few days ago that Travis had purchased Iron Scimitar in a claiming race when the disgruntled owner had given up on the temperamental animal. Travis had sensed something special in the horse. It was sometimes illogical, but trainers, jockeys, or owners would often believe in a horse everyone else had rejected. Frequently, that faith went unrewarded, and yet there was that rare fluke, the disregarded champion, the Count Fleet or Whirlaway. Finding a Cinderella horse remained a dream shared by everyone who was involved in Thoroughbred racing.

"He certainly doesn't have the temperament of an Oaks

horse, but he is Kentucky-bred," Mr. Martin said, obviously proud of his farm's reputation. In the racing world his horses were noted for their gentle, exemplary behavior. "Only why wasn't he in the south pasture? I sent Reanna there to see him."

"I moved Scimitar to the training track earlier this morning," David explained. "I wanted to start working with him. And since Excalibur needed a romp, I set him out."

Mr. Martin chuckled. "It sounds as though he got a romp, all right."

"Yes, he certainly did," Travis mumbled, still staring at Reanna with a confused frown. "Reanna," he murmured. "That's an unusual name."

It was an observation she'd answered hundreds of times. "I was named for my mother."

"Have you always lived in Kentucky?"

"What?" She touched her forehead in confusion. Why was he asking questions that required concentration?

"Where are you from?"

"From?" she echoed. "Oh, I used to live in Florida."

Somewhere in the deep recesses of her mind, it occurred to Reanna that she should be feeling something other than the numbness that gripped her, but she also knew her indifference was a defense mechanism that was keeping her from hysteria. She still couldn't comprehend it. For five years, she'd wondered who the nameless face belonged to, who the man was that had fathered her child, and all the while he'd been only a few miles away. She'd taught his niece at school for two years. The coincidence was unbelievable.

"When did we decide Jennifer needed a tutor?" Travis asked moments later. "I thought she had a minor learning disability."

To everyone else, it may have seemed like a casual inquiry, but Reanna could sense a sudden underlying hostility in his tone. His words had been clipped and cold. Surprised by the change in his attitude, she glanced up at him. He wasn't frowning anymore, and his features reminded her of a piece of stone. His face could have been carved out of rock, for all the expression she could read.

"We decided at the end of the school term," Jonathan told him. "Reanna suggested a tutor at our last parent-teacher conference. We were most fortunate that she was still available and could teach Jenny herself."

"Yes, that was most fortunate," Travis said softly.

"I'm certain we mentioned it," Jonathan went on. "It was right after you'd closed the syndication of Princelequa."

Princelequa was the stallion Martin Oaks had syndicated for stud earlier that year. Although he hadn't won the Triple Crown as a three-year-old, losing the Belmont Stakes by a neck, he'd gone on to be one of the all-time money winners in his fourth year of racing. Along with the entire city of Lexington and half the world, Reanna had closely followed his syndication. The deal had closed for several million dollars, and it was a well-publicized fact that it had also saved Martin Oaks from financial ruin. Unlike other farms, the Oaks was incorporated and depended solely on racing for its capital. The fire at Lakeland, which had destroyed most of its Thoroughbreds, had been a severe blow.

"Perhaps you were so busy you forgot," Jonathan was saying. "Anyway, Jenny's progress has been astonishing."

"Yes," Travis said again, "I'm certain it has been."

It was the way he said the word *yes*, as though it weren't affirmative, that bothered Reanna. Why was he angry? *She* was the injured party. He didn't even remember her. Or did he? Now that she thought about it, he'd seemed surprised when they'd been introduced. He'd stopped abruptly when he heard her name. And his curiosity about her geographic origin was odd, too.

Certain now that his cryptic remarks were a purposeful double entendre, she glanced sharply at him, searching his face for a glimmer of recognition. She was met by a cold, harsh stare that was more frightening than his earlier fury. The glacial gray of his eyes made her shiver, as though a sudden chill had enveloped her.

Just then, as if there weren't enough confusion, Jennifer barreled into the room, followed closely by Andy. Evidently, they had managed to avoid Mrs. Mackey's washcloth; they were both still filthy.

"Give me my truck!" Andy shouted, skirting perilously close to a table covered with expensive cut glass.

"Na, na, na, na, na," Jennifer shouted back. "You can't catch me."

"Whoa, there!" Jonathan reached for Jennifer while Mr. Martin, who was closer to Andy, grasped him firmly. "Shame on you," Jonathan admonished his daughter. "You mustn't tease Andy that way. Now give him back his truck."

Jennifer grinned and handed Andy the toy. "You still can't catch me," she declared.

"Can too!"

Mr. Martin chuckled. "And this little urchin is Reanna's son." He reached down to tousle Andy's hair fondly. "Andy, this is *my* oldest son, Travis."

"Hi, Andy." Although Travis quirked his eyebrow at his father in astonishment, he greeted the small child with a smile. To Reanna, the friendly gesture seemed inconsistent coming from the cold, hard man she'd just met.

"Hi." Andy wiped his hand on his muddy pants and held it out, just as he'd been taught.

He's dirty, Reanna thought as Travis clasped the grubby hand. *He's meeting his father for the first time, and he hasn't had a bath.* Then it struck her that the thought was totally illogical. After all, what did Andy's state of cleanliness matter?

"Should I call you 'mister'? or 'uncle,' like Uncle David and Uncle Jonathan?" Andy asked with abrupt candor.

"You can call me Uncle Travis."

"Do you want to see my magic fish? I just caught it at the pond. Jenny didn't catch one."

"That's because you took my worm off the hook," Jenny accused hotly.

Travis laughed and reached to tousle Andy's hair as Mr. Martin had done. "I'd be delighted to see your magic fish. What does it do?"

Reanna didn't hear Andy's response. The numbness that had seized her since discovering who Travis was abruptly began to recede as she glanced from father to son. She stared at the two of them, panic-stricken. Her hands began to tremble. When Andy had been born, although he hadn't resembled her, she'd been grateful that he hadn't inherited the dark features of his father. Now she realized he was the image of his grandfather, Mr. Martin. Why hadn't she noticed it before? There were the high cheekbones, the same deep blue eyes, the identical facial structure. Icy fingers of terror clutched at her heart. She didn't know anything about Travis Martin. What would he do if he found out that Andy was his son? Would he try to take the boy away from her? The thought was too frightening to contemplate.

"Andy, honey," she stammered, suddenly anxious to get him out of the room before they all noticed the resemblance. It was so obvious. And now Travis was studying their son with a strange intensity. "You're dirty. Let's go have a bath."

"Aw, Mom! Gramps said we could go fishing again." Andy turned to the old man. "Didn't you? Didn't you say we could go fishing?"

"Yes, I did," Mr. Martin admitted with a groan. "But

I'll tell you what. You go find Mrs. Mackey and get washed up first. We don't want to frighten the fish away."

"Can I come, too, Gramps?" Jennifer pleaded. "I want to catch a fish this time."

"Yes, yes, you can come, too, but no mud fights." Reanna started to clasp Andy's hand to lead him from the room, but Mr. Martin stayed her. "Let Thelma handle it. You've had an upsetting day."

Upsetting? That was an understatement. Reanna wondered in some detached part of her mind how much shock the human psyche could absorb and still function. Now that her protective foil of numbness had lifted, she felt like a caldron of compressed emotions, waiting to explode. She clenched her hands together tightly to keep them from trembling. She had to get control of herself.

"Really, Father," Travis said after the children had scampered away. "I'm surprised at your attitude. You never had much patience for children."

The old man smiled. "I have Reanna to thank for that. She won't allow me to grump at them." He laughed as Travis quirked an eyebrow again. "Don't be such a cynic, Travis. A leopard *can* change his spots, particularly as he ages. All those pills the doctor prescribed haven't helped me half as much as chasing after the children. Keeps a body young." Mr. Martin looked at Reanna and frowned. "Reanna, are you certain you're all right? You look pale."

She searched her mind for something to explain her sudden anxiety. All she could think of was leaving, of getting Andy out of this house before her secret was discovered. She wanted to run, to disappear.

"No, I'm fine. My wrist hurts, that's all." She pressed her fingers to her forehead. Everything was such a confused jumble. There was so much to be done. She had to leave. She had to pack. She had to get Andy. "If you'll excuse me now, I'd like to go upstairs," she murmured.

"There are some things I need to get done before . . ." Her thoughts were still coming to her in fragments. "I have some things to do."

Mr. Martin's frown deepened. "You don't look well, Reanna. Why don't you rest a bit?"

"The ch-children," she stammered, voicing her frantic thoughts aloud. She started to pace back and forth, trying to think clearly. "I have to get Andy."

"Don't worry about the children. Thelma and I can handle them for a while." Mr. Martin was looking more and more concerned as he watched her. "You've had a fall, Reanna. Are you certain you're not hurt?"

The old man's persistent solicitude made her realize her behavior was bordering on irrational. She clenched her hands at her sides until her nails dug into her palms, hoping the physical pain would help her regain her senses, but it took concentrated effort to stand still. "Oh, yes, thank you. I'll rest a bit, then."

As she turned to leave, her gaze was drawn to Travis. He was standing there, just watching her; and, although his expression was carefully blank, she had the oddest feeling he had convicted her of a crime. And there wasn't a hint of mercy in his bearing.

"Excuse me." Reanna tore her gaze from his and bolted up the stairs as fast as her feet would take her.

CHAPTER THREE

FOR THE NEXT HALF HOUR, Reanna raced around the room, pulling out her clothes and sticking them helter-skelter into suitcases. She refused to think about anything except getting out of the house as quickly as possible. With one fell swoop, she cleared her dresser, sweeping her belongings into a box. Then she emptied her closet, throwing her clothes onto the bed. Next she dumped the contents of a drawer into a suitcase and forced the top closed. She paused for a second, drawing in a deep breath. Her head was pounding with a combination of fear and anxiety, but she ignored the stabbing ache and started in again, dashing from one side of the room to the other.

Her frantic movements didn't stop until she slammed her hand in a bureau drawer. Her fingers hurt so bad that tears welled in her eyes. But deep down inside, she knew that wasn't why she was crying. In the space of a few hours, she'd experienced the entire gamut of human emotions. She was understandably distraught, but she was crying for the past. These tears had been locked inside for years, and at last she succumbed to them.

Reanna cried for the young girl who had lost her innocence to a stranger; she cried for her father; and she cried for what might have been. When there was nothing left but emptiness, she wiped her face and stared at her reflection in the mirror. She looked like a wild woman. Her long blond hair had escaped from its neat twist and tendrils were flying all over. Tiny wisps of hair curled tightly around her face. Her mascara was smeared, and her normally translucent skin was a pasty white. In contrast to the paleness of her face, her dark brown eyes shone large and luminous.

She smoothed her hair and sat down on the bed in the midst of her belongings, trying to think logically. Five years ago, she'd fled without thought to the consequences, but now she was a twenty-six-year-old woman who was responsible for a child. Yet she had to leave Martin Oaks. In her mind, at least that much was clear. She had to leave, and therefore she had to make plans.

But she also needed to be realistic. First, there was nowhere for her to go. When she'd come to work at the farm, she'd sublet her apartment. Consequently, she didn't have a place to stay. She would have to rent a flat; and considering her financial situation, finding something in her price range might take a while. Her checkbook looked like the payments ledger of the national debt.

Then there was Jennifer to consider. Reanna felt a responsibility to the child that went beyond the role of teacher. In the past month, she'd become a substitute mother for the little girl, and since it had helped the learning process, she'd allowed the relationship to flourish. But she'd thought she had all summer to prepare Jenny for her eventual departure. She couldn't leave without doing so.

Reanna chewed her lip thoughtfully as plans began to take shape in her mind. She would give Jonathan two weeks' notice. In that time, she could find an apartment, and perhaps even another position. Of course, she couldn't expect a new job to pay as well as tutoring Jennifer, but she would manage.

Not wanting to delude herself, Reanna admitted things weren't going to be easy. If she worked away from home, she would have to find someone reliable to care for Andy during her absence. Perhaps she could ask Miss Price if there were any other students who would benefit from part-time instruction for the rest of the summer. If she really ran into problems, Leona Price would take her in, but Reanna didn't want to depend on the headmistress. She'd been on her own for so long, she wasn't the type of person to impose. And she would have to offer the headmistress an explanation that would just perpetuate further lies.

For once, Reanna regretted not having formed close relationships here in Lexington. She'd been busy with Andy and her students, and most of the other teachers were single. They'd had so little in common that she'd made only casual friends.

She rose from the bed and started putting her clothes back in the closets. Two weeks. It seemed like a life sentence. Could she manage to avoid Travis for that period of time? There was really no other choice. She had to avoid him. So far, he hadn't remembered her. He'd thought she was a trespasser. It was only her guilty conscience that caused her to suspect he remembered her. She recalled every moment of that night they'd spent together with vivid clarity, and in her present distraught state she'd allowed her imagination to run rampant. He'd been drinking whiskey the evening they met, and had already been drunk when she'd introduced herself. And she'd only mentioned her name once.

She further reassured herself that even if Travis did eventually remember her, there was no way he could know Andy was his child. *She* had noticed her son's resemblance to his grandfather today because she *knew* Travis was Andy's father. There were thousands of children in the world with blue eyes and high cheekbones. No, there was no way Travis could guess that Andy was his son unless she told him; and of course she had no intention of doing that.

Two hours later, Reanna descended the stairs in search

of Jonathan. She had showered and changed into a light sundress, and had managed, by firm resolution and iron will, to regain control of her emotions. But she felt like a wooden statue. She took a deep breath and forced her lips into a tight smile before stepping determinedly forward. This would be the most difficult thing she had ever done, but she had to get through it.

At this time of day, Jonathan was normally in his studio, working. She started down the hallway, then stopped when she heard voices coming from the study. Immediately, she recognized Travis's husky tone. The laughter following his comment made her realize all four men were together. This wasn't the time to approach Jonathan with her resignation.

But just as she turned away to go find the children, Mr. Martin called after her, "Reanna. Come on in, my dear."

She hesitated only a moment. Though she didn't want to face Travis again, she couldn't very well be rude to the rest of the family. She took another fortifying breath and walked into the study.

"Are you feeling better after your rest?" Mr. Martin inquired.

"Yes, I'm fine now," Reanna replied, sitting in the chair he indicated. As soon as she entered the room, she realized Jonathan wasn't with them. She had to see him as soon as possible. Perhaps she could chat a few moments and then excuse herself. "Is Jonathan in his studio?"

"No," Mr. Martin said. "Don't you remember? He had an appointment at the gallery this afternoon."

"Oh, yes, I'd forgotten." Reanna's heart sank. It would be difficult just to leave the room abruptly. What excuse would she use? She shifted uncomfortably in the chair. Although she tried to avoid looking at Travis, unerringly her gaze was drawn to him. He had changed, too, she noticed. He was wearing casual slacks and an open-necked shirt that emphasized his lean physique. But it was his boots that drew her attention. They were dark brown, Western-style, and there was an eagle stitched on the front in multicolored threads. Ironically, it reminded her of a hawk, a predator poised for the kill.

"Where are the children?" she asked, tearing her gaze from the image. This was ridiculous. Now she was seeing visions.

"Thelma is giving them dinner. We caught several more fish. I'm afraid Andy wants to keep them in an aquarium, and I can't seem to convince him otherwise. He's a devil-ish little rascal," the old man went on, referring to Andy. "He and Jenny got into another mud fight." He laughed and glanced at his eldest son. "You know, Travis, he re-minds me of you at that age—always into some kind of mischief."

Travis turned to his father. "Devilment must be a trait all four-year-olds have in common," he answered dryly; then, after an infinitesimal pause, added, "I don't think we're related."

Reanna's heart lurched violently at his words. It was just an innocent remark, she told herself. He didn't *know*. He hadn't remembered her. She was certain of it, but nev-ertheless she clenched and unclenched her fists in silent fear.

"Well, I'm going to miss him when he goes back to school this fall," Mr. Martin went on. "I'm quite taken with him. I already feel like he's part of the family."

"You seem to be quite taken with the Widow William-son, too, Father," Travis said, still staring at her. His atti-tude suddenly reminded her of the eagle on his boots. It was as though he was mocking her, as though he was wait-ing. And she didn't want to think about what he might be waiting for. "I'm surprised you haven't convinced Jonathan or David to marry her yet."

It was common knowledge that Mr. Martin wanted his sons to settle down and produce some offspring to inherit the Oaks. Since she'd come here, Reanna had witnessed several sessions among the men; sessions that varied from teasing raillery to out-and-out matchmaking on the part of the old man, but the tone of Travis's remark bore no resemblance to the banter they normally engaged in. And if Reanna needed further proof that Travis was being rude, all she had to do was look at David. He was choking on his drink.

Reanna hissed on an indrawn breath. It was quite obvious now what Travis was waiting for. He had every intention of humiliating her. But why?

"What did you do up north, Travis?" David asked after he'd stopped coughing. "Take a course in rudeness?"

Travis merely smiled in answer. Mr. Martin, although he frowned, waved his hand and shrugged. "I was hoping to convince *you* to marry her, Travis," he said flippantly, "but now that she's met you, I doubt if she'd have you. First you frighten her half to death, and now you're being uncommonly brash. What's gotten into you?"

"Why, nothing, Father. I'm just trying to be polite to Mrs. Williamson. I haven't had the opportunity to get to know her as well as you. Our first meeting was brief, and rather . . . unconventional."

"Well, I think you owe her an apology," Mr. Martin persisted.

Travis flashed her another smile. "It seems that once again I must make amends. I'm terribly sorry for my discourteous manner. It's been a long and . . . extraordinary day."

But he didn't seem at all sorry, Reanna thought, and he appeared totally undisturbed by the anger in his father's tone. She had to remind herself that she was being overly sensitive. As far as Travis was concerned, their first meeting *was* brief and unconventional. She'd fallen off his horse. Yet it wasn't so much what he'd said as *how* he'd said it that disturbed her. And yes, it had been an extraordinary day.

"Jonathan is quite pleased with Jennifer's schooling," Travis went on conversationally. "You've made a great deal of progress in just a month."

"Jenny's very bright," Reanna said, keeping her tone even by sheer willpower. Was her perception distorted or was his attitude threatening?

"I understand it's common to misjudge a learning-disabled child's intelligence," he continued.

Reanna forced herself to remain calm. Her fears were making her touchy. He was merely being polite. Yet she couldn't help but wonder why he was being pointedly attentive to her. "Yes, they can be quite gifted although they learn best with a different approach from that used with ordinary children."

"And what is it exactly that you do to correct their problem?"

David laughed before she could respond. "That's like asking how you train a Triple Crown winner, Travis."

"I have to disagree with you, David. Fishing doesn't sound very educational. Or are we paying Mrs. Williamson to entertain Jenny? We could hire a nanny for a lot less."

"Reanna is highly qualified and has performed wonders with Jenny," Mr. Martin said. "If she wants to take her fishing, that's fine with me, and I'm certain Jonathan will agree."

By now, Reanna was feeling her temper rise. Travis's remark had been another deliberate insult. "Sometimes an activity that seems recreational is in fact an attempt to help coordinate motor function," she replied, the softness of her tone masking her underlying anger. "Which can be most beneficial for this type of child. They learn to bring that coordination to the classroom and apply it to something as simple as writing." She tossed her head back defensively.

"If you're truly interested, *Mr. Martin*, I could give you a brief course in the particulars of teaching a learning-disabled child."

"Have I offended you again?" he asked, flashing that mocking half grin at her. "I'm terribly sorry. I seem to be committing one faux pas after another today. And, please, call me Travis. We're not formal here. Besides, as Father says, you're practically *family*."

For a moment, Reanna felt her control slip. His apology had been as calculated as his original insult. But no one else seemed to detect the note of derision in his tone. Mr. Martin and David were both beaming at her. Reanna gritted her teeth and smiled politely. This was going to be more difficult than she had anticipated.

"Travis," Mr. Martin said, "speaking of family, did I tell you Cousin Lucy is getting married in September?"

As the conversation resumed without her, Reanna reassured herself once again that she was imagining the innuendoes she'd read into Travis's speech. He *had* apologized, and other than the way he'd inflected certain words, there was nothing to justify her suspicions. Because she remembered their brief affair and prayed he *didn't*, she was naturally tense.

Reanna pasted a smile on her face and listened to the men banter back and forth. Cousin Lucy's wedding seemed to be a source of contention among them, but since Travis had seemingly forgotten her presence, Reanna tried to relax. When the subject turned to horses, she started to shift again in her chair. Perhaps she could excuse herself now.

"I happened to run into Les Williamson the other day," Travis said to his father. "He was working with Glenn Robbins's colt, Bold Commander."

The casual statement fell on Reanna's ears like a sledgehammer. She felt her stomach lurch with alarm. How on earth would Travis Martin know her father? The coincidence was too incredible to believe. Then it dawned on her that this was a racing family. Her father was a respected horse trainer. Of course Travis would know him—they would *all* know him!

Suddenly, she longed to ask how her father was. She wanted to ask if he was well. It had been so long since she'd seen him, and he had a heart condition. It was nothing serious, but he tended to overwork and smoked too many cigarettes and drank too much coffee. Was he taking care of himself? She held her breath, waiting for tidbits of information.

"The colt by Bold Intruder?" Mr. Martin asked.

"Yes, he's a fine-looking animal, a little heavy, but with good configuration."

"Is he as fast as they say?"

"Faster. Although Les is being cagey and keeping him under wraps. He should give Iron Scimitar a run for the money."

Mr. Martin chuckled. "Even though he beat us once, I always did like Bold Intruder. Good breeding. He likes to misbehave, though, constantly nipping at the other horses."

It was a quirk, Reanna wanted to say, just a personality trait, like how some people growled at others but didn't mean anything by it. Underneath they were vulnerable. She had to concentrate on clenching her hands tight to keep the words inside.

"Yes, he was a bit of a trial. Les had some success with that spur bit he devised, but Intruder still likes to nip at the mares."

"Don't they all?" David asked. "Even Excalibur misbehaves when he's around a filly. Father, what's that old adage you keep repeating?"

"A woman will be a man's downfall, every time. Even

Secretariat lost a race because he was following a filly in heat."

Unexpectedly, David turned to her. "Williamson. Reanna, you wouldn't be related to Les Williamson, would you?"

Reanna let her breath out slowly. She liked David. Although he was just a few years younger than she was, he projected a certain naïveté; yet it was his earnest charm that caused people to trust and admire him. If he only knew the piercing distress his innocent question had aroused. "Williamson is a common name," she hedged.

"Isn't that a coincidence," Travis remarked. "Martin is a common name, too. But, of course, David, it is *Mrs*. Williamson."

He gave her a strange look as he spoke. It was odd; something in his bearing told her the conversation was just beginning. She felt her stomach start to flutter with foreboding.

"Of course, you're right," David said, moving to the sideboard to pour himself a drink. "I guess I wasn't thinking." Moments later, Reanna looked up, surprised, when he handed her a glass of dark amber liquid. "Here you go, Reanna. I'm sorry I forgot to ask you earlier to join us."

"Oh, no, thank you. I don't drink," she said. It was true. Since that night she'd gotten drunk, she hadn't so much as tasted liquor, but the words had come out all wrong. She had sounded hysterical. She clasped her hands in her lap and moistened her lips anxiously. She had to ignore Travis. She simply *had* to ignore him. Why was he watching her?

"Ah, but sherry doesn't count," Mr. Martin said. Since the doctor had recommended he drink a glass of sherry before dinner to increase his appetite, he had been extolling its virtues. "It will do you a world of good. You're much too thin."

"Really, Father," Travis said. "You mustn't force it on her. Perhaps Mrs. Williamson has an aversion to alcohol for some reason."

"I'm sorry, my dear. I didn't think," the old man quickly apologized. "Of course, if you'd prefer not to drink . . ."

Reanna drew her lips into another tight smile. Either she was still behaving irrationally and was reading far too much into his speech, or Travis was being very, very clever. He'd phrased his statement so that she was forced to explain her refusal. "No, no real reason. Perhaps I'll try some, after all."

She accepted the glass and sat quietly, hoping the conversation would resume without her. The mention of her father had upset her. Combined with her fear of discovery, it was more than she could bear without time to collect herself.

"I believe we have some strawberry brandy, Mrs. Williamson," Travis persisted. "If you'd prefer it instead."

Reanna jerked her head up sharply. He was sitting there in the chair smiling at her, but it wasn't an expression born of happiness or humor. It was more of a cynical smirk. A moment of panic gripped her. Why had he suggested such a strange drink?

"Strawberry brandy?" Mr. Martin echoed as though he hadn't ever heard of the beverage before. "I can try to find some."

"That won't be necessary. This will be fine," she said quickly. Did Travis know? Had he remembered after all? Oh, God, she'd been so certain he hadn't recognized her.

"Perhaps champagne, then," Travis suggested. This time, his smile faded and his eyes looked grim.

Reanna clutched the stem of her wineglass, trying to calm her frantic heartbeat. "No, no, thank you," she managed to say over the sudden dryness in her throat. "I loathe champagne."

"Really? That's strange." He propped one foot on the other knee and stared at her for an interminable moment. Then he tipped his glass to her in a half salute, exactly as he had that first night. "I would have thought you liked it, especially with strawberries. They have a magical quality, don't you agree?"

Reanna sat immobile, unable to speak. She clutched the stem of the wineglass tighter and tighter. He knew! He knew, and he was trying to trap her.

"You realize, Reanna," David interrupted, laughing, "that my brother likes to think he's a connoisseur where women's tastes are concerned. It seems you're wrong this time, old boy," he said to his brother. "Just like you're wrong about Cousin Lucy. Fair Stefanie may have had a fetish for strawberries and champagne, but that doesn't mean all women like them."

Travis kept his gaze fixed on her for several more breathless seconds, then turned to David. "Yes, I suppose you're right," he said. "In this instance I stand corrected. I can't imagine what made me think Mrs. Williamson would share Stefanie's tastes."

This time, Reanna couldn't quite calm herself. Although there seemed to be a logical explanation for Travis's statement, there were too many coincidences in this conversation. She fidgeted nervously with her wineglass. She felt like a cornered animal being stalked by a cunning hunter who was slowly closing in, but toying with her before the final, deadly strike.

And that feeling became more intense when Travis turned to her again. "You're quite young to be a widow, aren't you, Mrs. Williamson? Has your husband been dead for very long?"

"Several years," she murmured.

"That's unfortunate. Was it an accident that killed him?"

"N-no," she stammered, studying her glass of sherry intently. Usually, whenever the subject of her husband came up, people expressed their sympathy and let the matter lie. "No, he was killed in Belfast."

"Oh, was he a soldier? I didn't know we'd ever sent any troops to Northern Ireland. I was in Vietnam. It's an awful place, the jungles are steamy and insect-ridden, and it's hotter than hell."

Obviously, Travis wasn't like most people. He didn't know when to remain tactfully silent. "No," Reanna said. "He wasn't a soldier. He—he was a newsman."

She wondered suddenly if all unwed mothers made their imaginary husbands heroes. At the time of Andy's birth, it had seemed logical. She had based her fabricated past on current events, thinking that when Andy was grown she would have a poignant story to tell him about his father. Now it seemed silly.

"Are you sure your husband was the father of your son?"

"Pardon?" she asked, shocked at his question.

"I asked if you were sure your husband fathered your child. According to the news media, the only American journalist killed in Northern Ireland was buried ten years ago."

There was a sudden, surprised silence in the room as all three men stared at her. Reanna felt her heart start to thud with renewed distress. How could she have made such a careless error? And how could she have allowed herself to be backed into this corner? She searched her mind for a logical explanation for her blunder.

"Oh, did I say Belfast? I meant to say Beirut." God, she hoped it was current enough that he wouldn't notice it was several hundred miles away. "I'm not too good at remembering the names of foreign cities." Did her excuse sound

as lame to them as to her own ears? That statement made
her seem like a nitwit.

"Neither am I," Mr. Martin said, smiling at her sympathetically. "Was he famous?"

"My husband? No. No, he wasn't well known at all. He
worked for a small newspaper in Florida."

"His death must have been quite a shock for you,"
David said. "I remember when Jonathan's wife died, he
went through a tough period. It's the suddenness."

"Yes, it was quite difficult." Reanna set her wineglass
aside. It surprised her when Travis moved to the sideboard
and refreshed his drink. Somehow, she had expected him to
keep probing. Perhaps she could excuse herself now without appearing rude. She was about to speak when Mr.
Martin turned to her.

"Reanna, was your mother Celtic?"

While it seemed odd to sit here and discuss her heritage
when she wanted to leave, she couldn't just ignore his
question. Mr. Martin had been too kind to her in the past
two months. "Yes, how did you know?"

"You said you were named after her, and although I've
never heard it before, Reanna sounds Gaelic." He turned to
Travis. "You've been to Ireland and Scotland. Is it more
common there?"

For some reason, the question caught her off guard. She
hadn't expected Mr. Martin to draw Travis into the conversation, and she certainly hadn't expected the old man to
ask a direct question about her name. Her heart thundered
and her breath caught in her throat when she realized she
was waiting for his answer.

Travis, too, seemed to be waiting. He leaned back in his
chair and looked directly at her. "I've never heard the name
before."

Reanna stared incredulously at him. She felt that strange
chill envelop her again. He was lying. He *had* remembered

her, She knew it as surely as she was breathing.

"You don't look Celtic yourself," Mr. Martin went on. "More Swedish, I would think, except for your eyes. They're a most unusual shade of brown, almost golden."

"I resemble my father," she managed to say.

"Andy must resemble his father, too," Travis commented in a light, conversational tone. "He doesn't look a bit like you."

Reanna clenched her hands together so tightly her knuckles whitened. "No, he d-doesn't," she stammered. "He doesn't resemble his father at all."

Travis quirked a single eyebrow at her. "That's rather unusual, isn't it? I mean, genetically speaking, a child usually resembles one or the other of his parents. But perhaps you don't remember exactly what his father looked like. Maybe he was in Belfast too long."

There was an electric silence that only Reanna seemed to notice; a direct communication between her and Travis. Yes, he was trying to trap her. And he knew. She thought he was going to expose their past relationship any moment, but David had quickly turned to him.

"Travis, since we're on the subject of genetics, when are we going to breed Royelmaiden?"

"David," Mr. Martin spoke up, "Travis and I have both told you over and over, breed the best to the best and hope for the best. And that mare you want to breed with Princelequa is not the best."

"Dad, I think she'll throw fine foals. There's a nick there. I've researched it. Princelequa's get will have endurance, and Royelmaiden was sired by Sir Kelsy. You know damn well he's a speed horse."

"David, she's never won a race, and her sire wasn't a Stakes winner, either. Besides, she has a tendency to unsoundness."

It was an argument they'd carried on for days, an argument all horsemen carried on at one time or another. It was a proven fact, for various reasons, that only about twelve out of every ten thousand registered colts became successful sires, transferring their qualities on to their offspring. Good broodmares were equally hard to predict, but every horseman Reanna had ever known had his own theory with regard to both.

This time, however, she wasn't listening to the quarrel, and neither was Travis. He was staring at her with a mixture of derision and scorn. His smile was a direct challenge. She closed her eyes for a moment. Yes, he knew. She couldn't deny the obvious any longer.

"Are you going with us, Travis?" Mr. Martin asked. "David is in for a surprise."

Although she hadn't paid attention to their debate, it somehow registered in Reanna's panicked mind that the two men were going out to the office David had in the stables to look up information.

"I think I'll stay here and chat with Mrs. Williamson," Travis answered. "I'm certain she's not interested in David's research, and I've already seen his papers."

The intensity of her despair paralyzed Reanna, or she would have grasped the opportunity to escape. She sat glued to her seat while frantic thoughts flitted through her mind. What the hell was she going to do now? She had to leave, and she had to do it soon. She should have left hours ago. By staying, she had flirted with disaster, and now that disaster had found her and had exploded in her face. Intending to find Andy and run, she bolted from the chair.

"Sit down, Mrs. Williamson."

Something in Travis's tone made her stop. They were alone in the room. If she'd been apprehensive before, it was nothing compared to what she was feeling now. Her heart started to thud at breakneck speed.

"I said sit down. We're going to have our little chat now. What is it that you want?"

"What?" she echoed, clenching her hands together in distressed agitation. She *wanted* to *leave*.

"It's time we stopped playing this little game, Reanna. I know who you are. What I want to know is what you're doing here. You don't really expect me to believe your coming to Martin Oaks was a coincidence."

He was right. It seemed silly to continue the charade. It seemed silly, too, to insist that he believe she hadn't planned this encounter, yet it was the truth.

She met his piercing gaze with a defensive toss of her head. "But it *was* a coincidence."

His laugh was as cynical as his smile. "Come now, Reanna. I'm not the fool you take me for. You may have deceived the rest of the family, but you haven't deluded me with your sweet, innocent act."

"I didn't know," she said. "I didn't know when I came here that it was you. I—I didn't even know your name . . ." Her voice trailed away. It was hard even now to admit she'd slept with a man and hadn't known who he was.

"You knew damn well who I was that night, and you knew damn well who I was when you came here."

"No, I didn't," she insisted. "I didn't know your name. I didn't know who you were, and I didn't know anyone else at that party, either. I went with a friend."

"You and your little friend were quite sociable for two girls who didn't know anyone. There weren't any strangers at that party, Reanna."

"Shelly knew some people," she defended herself. "I—I didn't know anyone except Jack Carter."

"My picture was in every newspaper nationwide. Most of the world heard about the Lakeland fire, but you didn't know my name? It was the major topic of conversation for the entire evening."

"I heard about the fire," she said. "My father told me the next day, but even then I didn't know you were the man involved. I—I didn't read the papers."

"My, Reanna, you're awfully good at games. As I recall, you were good at them that night, too. You seemed to enjoy playing who's who. I must admit, your approach is unique. Not many women can lie as beautifully as you, or so expertly project that guileless air. Now, I suppose, you're going to tell me that when you recognized me today you were going to leave."

"Yes, that's true," she said quickly. "I was planning to leave."

"Oh, really, are you packed?"

"I thought—I . . . there were other considerations. I had planned to see Jonathan and give him my resignation. I wanted to give him notice."

"How thoughtful of you."

Reanna jerked her head up again. She was growing weary of his arrogance. She'd come here by mistake. Yes, it was an incredible coincidence, but nevertheless, it was a coincidence, and he was treating her as though she had ulterior motives.

"What exactly do you mean by that?" she asked sharply.

He laughed again. "I mean that I don't believe you. How much money do you want?"

"Money?" she echoed, thinking of all the years she'd struggled to support herself and Andy. That he thought she wanted money was degrading. He was treating her like a common prostitute.

"Money," he repeated dryly. "Surely the term isn't hard to understand? It isn't foreign, like Belfast or Beirut. You must be familiar with it. How much do you want?"

Hurt by the injustice of his accusations, her temper flared. "I thought half a million dollars might be an appropriate amount," she said angrily.

"Are you sure you're willing to settle for straight cash? Why don't you demand marriage? Or perhaps even you recognize that you'd need more than a night of passion for that kind of blackmail."

"Marry?" she repeated incredulously. "You think I came here to blackmail you into marriage?"

"Why else *would* you come here after all these years? I'm a wealthy man now. I've put this farm back together, and it's a well-publicized fact that I've just syndicated a stallion that has made me a multimillionaire. It's perfect fodder for an opportunist."

"Opportunist!" Reanna was repeating his words so often she was beginning to feel like a broken record, and with each passing moment her anger grew until it was a seething ball of fire within her. She stood up and glared at him. "Opportunist? Do you have any idea what I've endured because of that night we spent together? I made one mistake in my life, and I've paid for it every day since then. I lost my home and my father because of that night, and for five wretched years I've wondered who you were, who Andy's father—" Reanna bit her lip and stopped abruptly when she realized what she'd almost blurted out.

"Yes, go on," he said. "This is most interesting. You've lost your home and your father, and you were about to say something about Andy's father. You could at least get that story straight."

Reanna fingered her wedding band nervously, twisting it around and around her finger until she realized he was watching her. She clasped her hands in her lap. "N-nothing," she stammered. "It's not important."

"Not important? That's rather strange. Why would you have mentioned something that wasn't important?" His tone was laced with sarcasm, and his questions were sharp and probing as he continued, the hawk closing in on his prey. "Tell me about Andy's father, Mrs. Williamson, or should I say *Miss* Williamson? We both know you're not a widow. You've never even been married. It's all pretense, isn't it?"

Reanna stared at him through a red haze of fury. He was goading her, but she couldn't prevent her answer. She was too angry not to respond. "No," she snapped, "no, I'm not married, and I never was. And you know damned well who Andy's father is. *You're* his father."

The moment she said the words, Reanna regretted them. Now what was she going to do? It was too late to take them back, and suddenly she wasn't certain she wanted to retract them. No matter what happened, it wasn't possible that Travis could take Andy away from her. She was his mother. There were laws to protect her rights. She looked around her at the plush surroundings. Andy was the rightful heir to Martin Oaks. Didn't he deserve more than she could give him? Didn't he deserve his father's legacy?

"I believe I've underestimated you, Reanna. You're very clever, but I know Andy's not my child." For a moment, the abrupt conviction of his tone confused her. Reanna waited for him to tell her he was sterile or something equally as damning. "I wasn't your first lover. You could easily have been pregnant that night."

"I was a virgin that night," she said softly, feeling her face flame scarlet. Although discussing her virtue with this man was humiliating, she was determined to make him believe her. And he couldn't have insulted her more had he called her a name.

"Oh, come now, Reanna. Men are supposed to be able to tell those things. I would have noticed. Or are you planning to fall back on that old cliché about virgins who exercise vigorously?"

"I don't have to fall back on anything," she said, "and I don't have to defend myself. Whether or not you believe it, Andy is your child."

"All right, supposing I *was* your first sexual encounter. Do you expect me to believe I was your last? Do you really hope to convince me that Andy is the result of one brief night we spent together?"

Reanna tossed her head back. It was another direct insult, but she ignored it. She'd be damned if she'd continue to defend her morals. "Andy is your son," she repeated softly.

"If what Reanna says is true," Mr. Martin said from the doorway, "you will do the proper thing and marry her, Travis. My grandson will not be labeled a bastard!"

Reanna swung around to the old man, totally humiliated. She felt her face burn from embarrassment. It had been bad enough justifying herself to Travis, but Mr. Martin was a courtly southern gentleman. There were certain subjects that were taboo, and illegitimate children was one of them.

"I didn't mean to eavesdrop," he said, apparently recognizing her chagrin. "I was coming back for some records to show David." He turned to Travis. "Well?"

The single word vibrated with anger, but Travis merely leaned back in his chair and stretched out his long legs. "You needn't worry, Father. I'd be very willing to do the proper thing, but considering all her lies, I'm hardly inclined to take Reanna's word for something that is highly improbable."

He turned back to her and smiled again. It was amazing how cold such an expression could be, Reanna thought.

"I understand there are some sophisticated tests now that prove paternity beyond a doubt," he went on. "Of course, they also *disprove* paternity. Shall I make the appointment?"

More than anything, it was the way he said it that made Reanna determined to prove him wrong. Not that she would marry him when the truth was revealed, but he could acknowledge Andy as his child and provide for his education in a trust fund. She stood very still and looked straight at him.

"Yes," she said. "Yes, make the appointment."

Mr. Martin stood silently a few moments, then turned abruptly away. "It's time for dinner," he said, stalking from the room.

Surprised, Reanna stared after him. After all that had transpired this afternoon, how was she going to get through a family dinner?

"You've had lots of practice," Travis said as though he had guessed her thoughts. He moved toward the door as if to leave, then paused beside her. "I must admit, Reanna, your act is brilliant. But you can stop wringing your hands like the proverbial damsel in distress. No one's here to see you."

Reanna thrust her hands into her pockets while she looked up at him. This was the same man David revered, the same man who had looked at Andy with tenderness. "Why are you doing this? Why are you being so cruel?"

"Because, quite frankly, *Miss* Williamson, I think you're a scheming, conniving bitch who happened to remember that I had once bedded you, decided I was a meal ticket, came here and burrowed your way into my father's affections, and expected to trick me into marriage."

Before she realized what she'd done, Reanna slapped him. She watched, horrified, as a bright red handprint appeared on his face. Aside from a small muscle that twitched in his cheek, Travis didn't move. "You won't go through with it, you know," he said. "You won't go through with the tests."

"Oh, yes, I will." There was steely determination in her voice. "In fact, I can hardly wait."

CHAPTER FOUR

REANNA'S ANGER KEPT HER humiliation at bay throughout the rest of the evening. Whenever she wavered, regretting her impulsive admission and wanting to flee, all she had to do was remind herself of Travis's comments in the study . . . of his accusations. Vindication was uppermost in her mind. What a pleasure it was going to be to prove him wrong.

But the next morning, sitting in the laboratory having Andy's blood drawn, she felt like the ogre Travis had accused her of being. Except for an occasional checkup, Andy had seldom needed to visit a doctor since he was a baby. One look at the needle and he started to scream. As she held on to him tightly, comforting him, Reanna couldn't help but question her motives. Was she doing this for herself or for her son?

Her heart ached when, afterward, Andy climbed onto her lap, sobbing in giant gasps. He nestled against his mother and tucked his thumb in his mouth for comfort. She wanted to cry, too, as her guilt intensified. Andy hadn't sucked his thumb in months. Later, the Band-Aid the nurse drew a smiley face on became a badge of courage that he showed to the entire family, refusing to remove it, even for a bath.

That night, although Travis didn't wear a Band-Aid, Reanna's gaze was drawn to the small bruise on his arm where his blood had been drawn. He was dressed much the same as the day before, his shirtsleeves rolled past his elbows, exposing his tanned, muscular forearms, made even stronger by years of handling horses. He smelled faintly of horses, too, but his boots were shiny and spotless, the stitched eagle appearing golden in the dim lighting. For a second, she panicked. What if the results were negative? What would she do?

Then, when her gaze accidentally met his mocking gray one, she tilted her head high. There was no possibility of that happening, she thought. Andy was Travis's child. She knew that beyond a doubt. Yet deep down inside, there remained an anxiety that was difficult to quell. She felt as though she were on tenterhooks.

The next few days, Reanna tried to go about her daily duties as though nothing had changed. She worked with Jennifer and Andy for hours, planning outings, playtime, and learning experiences. Mr. Martin still joined them occasionally. There were times that Reanna caught him glancing at her in a puzzled, appraising manner. She could tell he, too, was wondering if this was all an elaborate scheme she had devised—a mercenary ploy. Surprisingly, his doubts didn't distress Reanna. After all, Travis was his son.

However, Travis's attitude *was* upsetting. Although he was marvelous with Andy, seeming genuinely to care for the child, with her he was angry and cynical. The paradox was bewildering. Reanna tried to avoid him as much as possible, and since that evening in the study they'd never been alone; yet they were drawn together by circumstances.

At the dinner table, Travis's mocking smile and snide remarks only reinforced his opinion of her. Mr. Martin, in his kindly manner, tried to keep the conversation flowing and kept smoothing over things that became awkward. If David and Jonathan sensed anything out of the ordinary, they didn't make an indication. Sometimes David would glance from Travis to Reanna and frown in confusion, but evidently both brothers were unaware of the developments of the past few days. In a way, Reanna was thankful. It was hard enough facing Mr. Martin and Travis. She didn't want David and Jonathan wondering about her, too.

By the third day of waiting, the underlying tension was nearly more than Reanna could bear. All she wanted was to get this over with, and she would leave Martin Oaks and the man who was driving her crazy. Travis would acknowledge Andy as his child, and she would go away with her son and live her life in peace.

But late that night when she was called into the study, she was more nervous than ever. Travis had been conspicuously absent all day. Though she hadn't asked, she'd known where he was. And when he'd come home earlier, Mr. Martin had immediately joined him, closing the door of the study. She couldn't help but overhear the hum of their angry voices.

Now Travis was alone, sitting at the huge oak desk. He was wearing a suit, she noticed, but his tie was unknotted, hanging loose around his neck, and his shirt was unbuttoned. When he looked up at her, the light from the lamp threw his features into shadow, making his expression seem harsh. Or perhaps it was just that he needed a shave. The stubble that darkened his face gave him a hawkish appearance.

Reanna sat in a chair across from him and folded her hands in her lap. "You wanted to see me?"

"Yes," he said, tossing a thick envelope across the desk toward her. "Apparently, I owe you another apology, Miss Williamson. It appears that there's one thing you didn't lie about . . ."

Suspecting the contents of the envelope were the results of the laboratory tests, Reanna didn't bother to reach for it.

She just looked at him, daring him to continue, wanting to hear the admission from his lips.

"Andy is my son."

Oddly, the triumph she'd expected to feel at those words didn't materialize. There was just a strange sensation of relief. She drew in a deep breath and closed her eyes for a moment in grateful appreciation.

"You seem surprised," Travis went on coldly. "Isn't that what you expected?"

The arrogance of his tone irritated Reanna. This time, *her* smile was derisive as she looked at him haughtily. "Yes, I guess I am surprised, but not at the results. I'm more amazed that you seem to believe it. Why haven't you questioned the results? Laboratories have been known to make errors."

Why was she doing this? Why was she casting suspicion on herself? He already thought she was an opportunist, a scheming bitch. But Reanna knew the reason she had asked those questions. It was out of spite. She wanted him to admit he was wrong. She wanted more than an offhand apology from him.

Travis quirked a single eyebrow as he leaned back in his chair. "Oh, but I did question the results."

Reanna felt as though he'd slapped her in the face. She stiffened with indignation. He couldn't even apologize without making her seem dishonest. "And?"

"The tests are conclusive." The damning statement didn't seem to disturb him a bit. He rose from the desk and went to the sideboard, pouring dark amber liquid into a glass. "Would you like a drink?"

"No," she retorted. How dare he act so snide! *She* was the injured party. She'd suffered all these years—struggling to raise Andy, to support him. "I don't drink."

"Not even to celebrate?" His lips twisted into a rueful smirk, and he leaned nonchalantly against the liquor cabinet. "Surely you'll have a drink to celebrate our impending marriage."

A pin dropping at that moment would have sounded like an explosion. Reanna was stunned. She sat very still and blinked in confusion. "Marriage?" she finally choked out. "You've got to be joking. What marriage?"

"Our marriage, my love. You are cordially invited to witness the exchange of nuptial vows between 'Mrs.' Reanna Williamson and Mr. Travis Martin this Friday in the palatial garden of Martin Oaks." Infuriating her more, he saluted her with his drink and bowed formally. "Do you think you can be ready, my blushing bride?"

"You're joking." Reanna couldn't believe it. It was too incredible to be true. Marriage? The suggestion had to be an elaborate ruse—a scheme to get back at her. Rather than pleasure, her short laugh was from shock. "You've got to be joking. We can't be married."

"Oh? And why is that?"

Reanna clenched the arms of the chair. It was the way he phrased things that incensed her. "Stop!" she said angrily. "Just stop patronizing me! You know perfectly well why not. I should think marrying me is the last thing you'd want to do."

"That's quite true, Reanna." He seemed amused by her outburst. He calmly capped the decanter of liquor and turned to her. "May I call you Reanna? Considering the circumstances, it seems silly to use formalities."

If he hadn't paused, waiting, she wouldn't have bothered to answer. He was so damned arrogant! "For godsake, I don't care what you call me," she lashed out, "just get to the point."

Maddeningly, he sipped his drink and watched her. "Yes, the point. As I was saying, you're absolutely correct, Reanna. Marrying you *is* the last thing I want to do. Unfortunately, there doesn't seem to be another choice."

"That's absurd," she countered, still in a state of stunned disbelief. "Of course there's another choice."

"You seem awfully astonished, Reanna. I thought you'd be delighted by this turn of events. You're getting what you wanted. You did come here to marry me, didn't you?"

There was a tense moment while they glared at each other, two strong personalities ready to clash. It disturbed Reanna that his opinion of her was so low, but more, it angered her. Yet she had to control herself. She had to make sense of this.

"If what you're saying is true," she answered, calming her temper by sheer willpower, "why do you suppose I waited five years to force you into marriage?"

"That's easy. I've only recently become wealthy. What fun is it to marry someone who isn't a multimillionaire?"

"You're so determined to prove me a gold-digger," she retorted. "Do you mind if I ask why you would play into my hands? Why would you do something so absurd? If we get married, all this becomes mine." She gestured around the room. "I'm certain it's worth more than half a million dollars cash."

"Oh, but that's where you're wrong, Reanna." Equally controlled, he handed her another envelope. "This is called a premarital agreement. I'm sorry to have to ask you this, my dear, but before we exchange our nuptial vows, you will sign it."

He wasn't sorry at all. That was evident in his every word, every gesture. Reanna looked at the papers through a red haze of rage. She was innocent. It had just been proven that Andy was his child, and yet, no matter what she did, he insisted on viewing her as a villain.

"What's the problem, Reanna? You seem upset. Aren't things going as you'd planned?"

It was senseless to keep trying to defend herself. She placed the papers on the desk. "This is crazy. Why are you doing this? Why have you even suggested this—this absurd arrangement?"

"Quite simply, to provide for Andy," he said.

"So provide for Andy," she shot back. "You can do that without marrying me."

He pushed from the bar and crossed back to the desk in easy strides. Then, picking up a statue of a horse, he studied it for a long moment. "Ah, yes, I suppose that's possible. I suppose I could provide for Andy in another way. Let's see, perhaps I could give you some money?"

Reanna stared at him. Did he mean it? All she wanted was to leave here and get on with her life. She leaned forward earnestly. "I'm sure we could work something out. Just a small amount would be fine. I don't need much."

"You're so agreeable when it comes down to cash." The abrupt coldness of his expression was frightening. His features were a dark mask of animosity. Chills of fear traversed her spine as he nailed her with his gaze. "I thought you would be. Just for the record, Reanna, I have no intention of giving you money, now or ever."

It was frustrating that he kept misconstruing her motives. "Travis, I didn't mean it when I said I'd take half a million. I was being flip. You made me angry. Just give me enough to provide for Andy's college education, and I'll go away. I really don't want anything for myself from you. I didn't mean for this to happen. I didn't come here—"

"Your humble act is touching, Reanna," he cut in, "but I don't believe a word. As I told you the other night, your price is a bit steep for a single night of passion."

"And so is marriage to a man I loathe!" she retorted, unable to prevent her temper from skyrocketing out of control. What did she have to do to convince him? "How many times must I tell you, I don't *want* your money? If you don't trust me you can put it in a fund. I won't touch it!"

He gave a harsh half laugh. "All right, Reanna. Even if I didn't question your motives, how do you suggest I give Andy my name? You do want me to claim him as my son, don't you?"

She stood abruptly, pacing the floor. At last she was making headway. "All you have to do is file a legal petition claiming him as your child."

"And inform the entire city of Lexington and most of the country that Andy was born out of wedlock? What would that do to him a few years from now? He's an innocent child. How would he feel about being labeled a bastard?"

The past few days Reanna had avoided thinking about that, conveniently pushing the horrible stigma to the back of her mind. Andy was her son, her flesh and blood, and she was fiercely protective of him. It would be devastating to any child, she finally admitted. No longer angry, in fact nearly void of feeling, she sat back down in the chair, trying to think clearly. Marriage—that was the last thing she'd expected to consider.

"If I file a legal claim for Andy without marrying you," he went on quietly, "we may as well take out a newspaper ad informing everyone of the circumstances of his birth. If we're married, it will seem logical that I would want to adopt him."

Reanna felt defeated. Though she hated to admit it, now that her anger had dissipated, what he said made sense. "It seems ridiculous for us to marry just to protect Andy. Isn't there some other way?"

"No. This way is really quite simple. We will pretend to have fallen madly, passionately in love; we'll be married, and I'll adopt Andy. After an acceptable period of time, we can develop irreconcilable differences and divorce."

For the first time, she looked at him with an emotion other than anger. His weary, resigned expression made her feel strangely sympathetic. "You don't want to do this, Travis, not any more than I do," she said softly. "Your father is coercing you into it, isn't he? You were arguing before."

"My father is an old man, Reanna." With a sigh, he held the statue up again, turning it, examining it; then he put it back down and looked directly at her. "You've given him something he's always wanted—a grandson to inherit the Oaks. And, yes, he does want this marriage, but he can't force me to do anything I don't want to do. This was my decision."

Reanna studied him for a long time, searching for clues to explain his odd behavior. Why would a man like Travis Martin propose this preposterous arrangement? Was it because of Andy? He cared for their child. The rapport between father and son had been immediate and binding, but she found it hard to believe he would sacrifice his freedom to rectify an old wrong. He hadn't even known about Andy.

"Travis—" She paused, not knowing how to phrase her words. Though she hated the choice, his solution was the only logical answer to the dilemma. It was galling to admit he was right, but she wasn't so stubborn that she couldn't recognize and assess their options. She didn't want Andy to be hurt. If she insisted that Travis acknowledge him without a marriage, her son would suffer. But Travis hadn't exactly proposed in the traditional sense. What should she say?

"Don't bother trying to use that guileless routine on me, Reanna. I know what you're after, and I'm not easily deluded. No matter how you try, no matter what you do, you won't get a thing when you leave here."

Suddenly, Reanna seethed with more anger than she'd felt in her entire life. But she forced herself to smile politely.

"Of course you're right, Travis. I should have known I couldn't deceive you." She snatched the papers and scrawled her name across the bottom. "Since this is all you're offering, I'd be a fool not to take it, but I'm certain I'll find a way to get something. Don't forget, a schemer like me can be quite devious. I assume I will be given a copy?"

Travis smiled, yet his eyebrows were raised in a dark slash across his forehead, as though he was surprised by her rash admission. Under his intense scrutiny, she nearly wavered, wanting to blurt out that it was all a lie, but then he spoke. "Yes, I'll be delighted to give you a copy, as soon as it's notarized."

"Fine." She started to leave, abruptly turning back and pausing with her hand on the doorknob. "I have only one other question, Travis. As you've discovered and so eloquently pointed out these past few days, I'm very good at duplicity. But how are you going to manage? Won't you find it difficult to pretend we're madly and passionately in love?"

For one breathless moment, she watched something flare in his eyes, some inexplicable emotion that was strangely disturbing. His gaze burned through her. "Is that a challenge, Reanna? Let me assure you, when I put my mind to it, I can be very convincing."

The following morning, Reanna discovered just how convincing he could be. She'd spent a restless night, and arrived in the dining room late. Mr. Martin, Jonathan, and David were already eating.

"Reanna and Travis?" David was saying. "That's incredible! They've barely spoken a civil word to one another since Travis came home."

Reanna paused in the doorway, feeling her face burn with embarrassment. Of course it was incredible. A better word choice was "unbelievable." How would they ever pull this off? But then Travis walked into the room.

"Which just goes to show you, David," he said, coming up behind Reanna and encircling her waist with his arms, "that a person's behavior isn't always indicative of their true feelings. I assure you that despite our little tiffs, Reanna and I are very much in love. Right, my sweet?"

Jonathan's fork had clattered to his plate, and David was staring at her with openmouthed shock, waiting for her reply. She glanced at Mr. Martin in an appeal for help, but he was grinning from ear to ear. Surely he wasn't so old and infirm that he didn't realize this was an act!

"Yes," she managed to say, smiling wanly at the trio of men while Travis pulled her next to his hard thigh. She could hardly deny his statement.

"Well, isn't this wonderful news? Congratulations, my boy," Mr. Martin boomed out. "You and Reanna make a fine couple. I gather you've worked out your differences?"

"Yes, Father, Reanna and I have managed to work out our differences. In fact, we've reached a total accord. Ours will be a model marriage." Travis pushed aside her long blond hair and kissed her lightly on the neck, as though they were lovers. "Right, honey?"

This was ridiculous, she thought. Wasn't he overdoing it just a bit, calling her honey and sweet, kissing her? And his innuendoes! Well, two could play at this game. She squirmed around in his arms and smiled at him.

"Have you had breakfast, dear?" she asked sweetly. "Here, let me get you some coffee. As a model wife, I want to start assuming my duties right away."

A surprised expression crossed his features, but he quickly recovered, sweeping her against him. To an observer, it would look as though she had initiated the embrace, and although he lowered his voice, his suggestive words rang clear. "Ah, love, it's unfortunate, but there are certain duties we're going to have to exercise restraint about. Do you mind terribly . . . waiting?"

Reanna felt her face flame. She wanted to kick him, but she jerked from his arms and turned to the sideboard, piling food on their plates. When she tried to hand Travis his breakfast and sit across the table, away from him, he patted the seat nearby. "Come, come, my love, sit here. Don't be shy, now. People might think you're afraid of me."

Gritting her teeth, she sat down and moved her chair away slightly, but Travis flung his arm across her shoulders, pulling her closer. What in the world was he trying to prove? Was this another deliberate attempt to humiliate her? If so, he was succeeding. She squirmed, trying to dislodge his hand without being conspicuous. It was a fruitless effort. His arm was like a steel band.

"Well." Jonathan cleared his throat and smiled at them. "When is the happy day?"

"Friday." Travis played his fingers along her throat in an intimate caress, as though he couldn't keep from touching her, and glanced down at her. To everyone else, it must have seemed like a tender expression of love. "Once we revealed our true feelings for each other, we just couldn't wait."

Reanna clenched her jaw to keep from blurting out the truth. Everything Travis was saying was accurate, but he was twisting the facts into sexual innuendoes. He made it sound as if they could hardly wait to get into bed with each other. Once he had accused her of being good at playing games. It was obvious that he was the expert!

"So soon?" David asked, clearly surprised. "What about Iron Scimitar's training? Won't it be delayed? You'll be going on a honeymoon."

"If we were to wait for an opportune time, we'd never be married," Travis answered. That was certainly true. As a Thoroughbred owner, he was busy all year round.

"We've decided to forgo a honeymoon. Besides," he added, caressing Reanna's throat again, "everything we need is here."

What an incredible thing to say! Seething with resentment, Reanna glanced sharply at him. If he made one more reference alluding to a bed, she swore she would pick up his plate and dump it over his head. She started to speak when Mr. Martin broke in.

"We'll have to make certain they can get away later, David." Obviously smoothing over the conversation, he cleared his throat and went on, "What was Scimitar's time yesterday? Weren't you going to work him fast?"

"Huh!" David said. "We could barely get him to gallop. That horse has a mind of his own, and the nastiest disposition of any animal I've ever worked with. Did Travis tell you he bit his groom last night?"

Reanna was grateful when the subject turned to Iron Scimitar's training. She sat still and listened, tolerating Travis's hand along her shoulders only because it would look odd if she objected. At least he wasn't discussing their relationship now.

"Scimitar bit Charlie?" Mr. Martin asked.

"He's developed some bad habits we're going to have a hard time overcoming," Travis answered. "But despite his dispostion, I know he's a responsive animal. I can't figure out why he won't run now, unless Marc Callahan spoiled him and tried to bring him along too slowly."

"I'll bet Callahan couldn't figure it out, either," David said. "That's probably why he sold him. Now we're stuck with an expensive horse who does what he damn well pleases."

"I followed him closely in the early part of the season, David. I was impressed then, and I'm still impressed."

"The only race he won was his maiden."

"By fifteen lengths against some of the best two-year-olds in the business, and he wasn't in full stride. He's got speed and endurance. We just have to work with him. Personally, I think he's lazy. And you know damn well that's been a problem with some of the best colts. Look at the history of Gallant Fox."

While he spoke, Travis caressed her shoulder with one hand. Because it was unbearably hot, Reanna had worn another sundress today. Strangely, his fingers on her bare skin sent odd sensations through her. She sat paralyzed, listening.

"If you're comparing Iron Scimitar to Gallant Fox, forget it," David shot back. "That horse was a little spoiled, liked to look at the sights, maybe, but he was a champion."

"Not until his three-year-old campaign," Travis insisted.

"Whatever Scimitar's problem is," Mr. Martin commented, "it's going to take patience and a firm hand to correct. Are you certain he's worth it, Travis?"

"I believe in the horse."

David gave an expansive sigh. "If you're so sure of this colt, why don't you turn him over to Bud Stevens?"

It was a rare owner who worked with his horses beyond the yearling stages. As a business, farms were too large and too diverse, and most owners ran a variety of horses year round, not only in the well-known, prestigious races, but in stakes or handicaps all over the country. A farm with hundreds of horses couldn't possibly handle all the animals without outside help, so at their second birthday, nearly all Thoroughbreds were placed in the hands of a trainer who took them from track to track, campaign to campaign. Bud Stevens was one of the oldest and most respected trainers in the horse-racing world. He handled an entire stable of Martin Oaks horses.

"Bud refuses to touch him. I'm afraid if I expect to win with Scimitar, it's up to us."

Thinking he was immersed in conversation, Reanna

leaned forward to escape his hand, but Travis moved, too, slinging his arm casually around her neck. Moving in light circles, his fingers caressed her torso, coming unbearably close to the soft curve of her breast. At his touch, something warm and curiously exciting transfused her. She felt flushed. The incredible part was that she wasn't blushing. Somehow she knew David was talking, yet she had to pay careful attention.

"I don't know, Travis. You're a damn good trainer. Everybody knows that, but Scimitar's already lost most of the important races as a two-year-old. Surely you don't intend to put him back on the circuit? From what I've seen, he just doesn't have the potential of a Triple Crown candidate. We'll be lucky if he wins a couple of big stakes next year."

"I plan to enter him in the Sanford in August."

"You've got to be joking," Jonathan spoke up. "That's only three weeks away!"

Reanna was surprised, too. All race horses ran daily, sometimes breezing, sometimes galloping, but their campaigns were spaced every few weeks. Iron Scimitar had raced recently, and if Travis ran him so quickly, there was a risk of burning him out. In addition, that particular race was limited to the best two-year-old horses. The entrance fee alone amounted to several thousand dollars—a large sum to spend on an unproven horse.

Evidently, David agreed with her. "I wonder if this horse isn't just a pipe dream," he said. "Sure, he's got potential, but the Sanford . . . ?"

Travis frowned thoughtfully. "Perhaps you're right. We'll just have to wait to see. I intend to race him."

The abrupt conviction of his tone silenced all three men. David shrugged. "It's your decision. Aren't you hungry, Reanna?" he asked her a few moments later. "You haven't touched your food."

"Oh." She'd been so absorbed by the conversation she had forgotten to eat. She picked up her fork.

"I hope it's not premarital jitters," Travis said, glancing at her with feigned concern. He took the fork from her hand. "Here, let me help you. I certainly don't want my lovely bride collapsing from starvation."

His mock solicitude made Reanna furious all over again. Why was it that he could goad her into irrational anger so easily? "I can manage," she snapped, pushing away the food.

"Now, now, love," he chided, cradling her hand. "You mustn't be so testy. What will people think?"

More annoyed with herself for allowing him to provoke her than with Travis, she returned his derisive glance. "Goodness, I hadn't thought about that," she replied sweetly. "I'm terribly sorry. I wouldn't want to do anything that might give the wrong impression. Do you forgive me? I am so nervous."

Travis smiled tenderly, playing the game to the hilt. "Of course, darling. I understand."

"Talk about a chameleon changing colors," Jonathan said with a hearty laugh. "Love seems to have bamboozled you, big brother. I guess there's no longer any confusion regarding your feelings, and as much as I'd like to stay and witness your comeuppance, I have to get to my studio. Reanna? Will you be able to manage Jenny this week?"

"Yes, of course, Jonathan. Just because I'm—I'm—" Voicing it aloud made it seem so definitive. Gone was her bravado of moments ago. And Travis's hand, holding hers, burned into her flesh. "—I'm marrying Travis, there's no reason for anything to change between Jenny and me. I'll still work with her."

"Well," David spoke next, "I have to get to the stables. Travis, are you coming?"

"In a moment." Travis looked at her, and from his expression, she could tell he intended to agitate things further. "I can't leave without saying good-bye to Reanna."

She nearly exploded as he brought her hand to his lips. This was ridiculous. There was no need to go this far! She conceded the game—if that's what this was. Fueled by exasperation and nearly at the end of her endurance, she kicked at him under the table. She wanted to scream with fury as her sandaled foot connected with his hard boots.

He merely smiled. "Each second without you will be an eternity, love. Until tonight."

Reanna had to restrain the impulse to stand up and screech at him like a fishwife. He was enjoying this! Relishing every moment. "Yes, until tonight," she managed to retort.

He ignored the warning in her tone as blithely as he had ignored her physical blow. "Now be certain to eat your breakfast, love. You have to keep up your strength."

Flashing her another sardonic smile, he strolled to the door with a chuckling David at his side.

"Jonathan's right," the younger brother commented, "you sure are smitten. If I wasn't seeing it myself, I wouldn't believe it."

Neither do I, Reanna thought, *and I'm enduring it.* Given a choice, she definitely preferred the cynical man she'd first met to this display of sickeningly effusive behavior. But why couldn't his family see through the façade? Mr. Martin was still beaming his approval.

"I must go, too," he said now. "I told Travis I would notify the family. There are a lot of calls to make." He paused a moment. "I'm glad you and Travis have worked this out, Reanna. Considering the circumstances, it's the only choice."

So he did see through the ruse. "I know," she said softly. "Thank you for understanding and being so supportive. This must be difficult for you."

"Andy's my grandson. That makes it worthwhile." The old man started to leave, then abruptly turned back. "Reanna, he's a good man. A bit hard sometimes, but he's fair. If you're patient, he'll come around."

What in the world did he mean by that? Reanna wondered. It sounded more like he was talking about a horse than his son. Sighing, she went into the kitchen to find the children. A few minutes ago, she'd heard Jenny and Andy arguing.

Usually spotless, the room was a mess, and in the middle, immersed in a cookbook, stood Thelma Mackey. She looked up when Reanna entered, and beamed.

"Oh, Miss Reanna, it's been so long since I've prepared for a wedding, I've forgotten all the traditional foods." She leafed through the thick book. "What are those little things called? I think they're French, and they're shaped like tiny rosebuds. I do so want to serve them. Maybe I should look under liver pâté."

"Thelma, you don't have to fuss." Reanna felt even guiltier. This wedding was a sham, a farce, and Thelma was obviously anticipating the event of the century.

"Oh, I'm so happy for you and Mister Travis, Miss Reanna. And Master Andy, isn't he going to be glad?"

"Thelma, please don't call us Miss Reanna and Master Andy."

"What will I call you then?" The housekeeper looked genuinely confused.

"Reanna and Andy will be fine."

"But that seems disrespectful." Her frown deepened. "You're going to be the mistress of the house."

Reanna sighed again. "You have my permission, Thelma. Please call us Reanna and Andy. Now, where are the children?"

"Out back on the porch, coloring. Perhaps they're listed under canapés," she went on, leafing through the index.

Then she smiled excitedly. "Oh, Miss Reanna, it will be so good to have a mistress of the house again. When Miss Rachel—that was Jonathan's wife, you know—when Miss Rachel was alive, we had such parties!"

"Really?" Reanna commented, listening politely. Thelma had been kind to her. It wasn't the housekeeper's fault that she was in a testy mood.

"Oh, yes, and I knew it all the time," Thelma went on in her undaunted manner. "I could tell by the way Mister Travis looked at you that we'd be having a wedding soon. And I'd almost given up on him ever finding someone and settling down. Why, half the belles in Lexington have been after him for years, but Mr. Travis always swore he wasn't going to fall into any of their traps."

Still talking, she placed the cookbook aside and bustled over to the stove to rescue a pot of food that was boiling over. "He was engaged once, you know, when he was younger. It was the oddest thing. I never did understand it. One day Miss Lysandra just up and married someone else. It was right after those horses came down with the virus. We almost lost the farm, and then just when it was going right again, there was that fire. Such a shame, losing all those horses, and there wasn't enough insurance. I tell you, Mister Travis worked hard to put it back together again. He was just bound and determined that Martin Oaks wouldn't be sold. He was different after that, though. And he developed a terrible reputation with the ladies. So many young girls came and went, I couldn't keep track of them. Let's see, there was Stefanie—"

"Thelma, why do you think Travis is marrying me?" Reanna asked suddenly. The moment she spoke, she wondered why she had posed such a question. The housekeeper could hardly guess Travis's motives.

Thelma stared at her incredulously. "Why, because he loves you, why else?"

Indeed, why else?

"I knew the minute I laid eyes on you that you would be perfect for Mister Travis. You're opposites, you know. Opposites attract."

"Excuse me, Thelma." After what the housekeeper had said, Travis's proposal made less sense than ever, but Reanna didn't have time to ponder it. "I have to see to the children."

"Oh, Miss Reanna, have you decided on a gown yet? It's going to be so beautiful. The ceremony's going to be in the garden, you know. All the shrubs and plants are in full bloom. We've never had a garden wedding before. What am I saying? We've only had one wedding around here, and that was Mister Jonathan's. Fine ceremony that was, too. Such a shame Miss Rachel had to pass on so suddenly like that. I wonder if Mister Jonathan will ever find someone else? He's so involved in his painting, you know."

Thelma never needed anyone to converse with. She always posed her questions and answered them in the next sentence. And Reanna was thinking about a gown. What *was* she going to wear? She couldn't get married in jeans, even if the ceremony was a sham. She would have to buy something, and that would deplete her funds further. She sighed. "I have to go, Thelma."

"Oh, yes, I'll see you later, then. Perhaps this afternoon we could go over the menu? I'm cooking everything myself. Can't trust caterers, you know, to give you good service for something so important." She picked up the cookbook again. "Maybe the rosebuds are listed under canapés."

Thelma was still talking when Reanna left. Jenny and Andy were on the porch, still coloring, thank the Lord. Unsupervised, the two of them together could cause a great deal of mischief. For the next several hours, Reanna worked with Jenny. One of her problems as a learning-disabled child was seeing common words backward. To her, *what* looked like *tahw*. Using flash cards, they went over and over specific problems. Jenny was getting so good these days she hardly made a single mistake.

But Reanna was only half concentrating. She was more concerned about how to tell Andy that she was getting married. How would her son react? For years, it had been just the two of them. Would he be upset? Would he think she was deserting him?

As Thelma predicted, Andy was thrilled.

"Uncle Travis is going to be my daddy?" he said when Reanna finally just announced it. "Oh, wow! That's neat. Maybe he can take me fishing, instead of Gramps."

Surprisingly, Jenny's eyes weren't aglow with the same happiness. Her lips formed a pout. "How come you don't marry my daddy?" she blurted out. "So I'd have a mommy."

"Oh, Jenny." Reanna enfolded the child in her arms. She had been so busy trying to absorb the developments, she hadn't even considered the effect it would have on the young girl. "I'll still love you. I'll always love you, no matter what. I'll be your aunt."

"I don't want an aunt! I want a mommy! I want you to be my mommy."

"I know," Reanna said softly, "and maybe one day you will have a mommy, but your daddy and I can't get married. We aren't in love with each other."

Jenny considered this a moment. "Are you and Uncle Travis in love?"

It was just a small lie, Reanna told herself. "Yes. Yes, we are. And we're going to be a family, Uncle Travis, Andy, and I, but I'll still be here. We're going to live here."

"You're not gonna leave?"

"No, I'm not going to leave," Reanna reassured her, "at

least, not now. And I'll be here when school starts. Now, won't that be fun? I was going to have to leave when school started."

If her marriage to Travis lasted that long, she thought. She had to start preparing Jenny for her departure. The child was entirely too dependent on her, but right now, all she wanted to do was offer reassurance.

"Yuck, school," Andy piped in. "Mom, I don't want to go to school. I want to stay home and play. Maybe when he's my daddy, Uncle Travis will let me stay home."

Jenny, more sophisticated at six, gave Andy a haughty look. "If you don't go to school, you'll be dumb."

"Won't neither!" Andy countered. "It's girls that are dumb."

"Andy!" Reanna sharply corrected. Where had he gotten that attitude? She'd certainly never taught him that!

"It's all right," Jenny said, "he's a boy."

Perhaps it was just their ages, Reanna thought. At four and six, boys and girls naturally fought. She sighed and opened the textbook, but Jenny made several errors. Things she had already learned and managed well were suddenly almost more than the child could handle. Reanna could tell she was still petulant. Was the wedding that upsetting? More to the point, what could she do about it?

"Jenny," she said in a flash of inspiration. "How would you like to be my flower girl? I would love for you to walk down the aisle with me, and we could buy you a special dress."

"Could I?" the little girl asked, brightening.

"Of course," Reanna said. There was no doubt that Jonathan would approve. And if Travis objected to her expenditure, she'd buy the dress out of her own money. "It's the next best thing to being a bride."

If you were marrying for love, that is.

Jenny was ecstatic. "Okay!" she said enthusiastically. "I get to be a flower girl."

"Well, now that that's all settled," Reanna went on, "why don't we take the rest of the day off? And as a special treat, we'll do whatever you children want. You choose."

"Let's go see the baby horses!" Andy said, the marriage forgotten.

"Yeah!" Jenny echoed. "Let's go."

Reanna smiled. She should have known. Where Jenny and Andy were concerned, there was no other choice. They loved watching the young foals that had been born this spring frolic in the pasture with their mothers. They would stare at them with fascinated longing. Jenny, although she had her own pony, wanted a real horse, and Andy was just as bad. They would try to talk the grooms into letting them ride the Thoroughbreds, and make a total nuisance of themselves. Usually, except for special days, Reanna kept them away.

"All right, but just for a little while."

While Jenny and Andy leaned on the fence, calling to the foals, Reanna looked toward the track where Travis and David were working with Iron Scimitar. Although she could see him, Travis seemed unaware of her presence. She watched from afar as he saddled the horse, easily imagining his strong hands and soothing voice calming the skittish animal.

After a bit, bored by being ignored by the horses, the children scampered off in the direction of the barns. Thinking they would head for the kittens that had just been born, Reanna followed. But suddenly Jenny spotted Travis walking up the knoll toward the complex.

"Uncle Travis! Uncle Travis," she called, running off in his direction. Andy barreled after her.

Travis, though he was clearly surprised by the children's presence, smiled and scooped them up in his arms. "Well, what are you two doing down here? Aren't you supposed to be studying?"

"I don't gotta study," Andy answered. "Jenny's the one. She's gotta study."

"I don't gotta study," Jenny retorted. "I *want* to study. And I'm going to be a flower girl." It all came out in a single, excited breath.

"Yeah, and you're gonna be my daddy," Andy added.

"Yes, Andy, that I am," Travis answered gravely. "Are you going to like that?"

"Oh, boy!" Andy answered, throwing his arms around his father's neck. "Am I! We can go fishing."

Travis laughed, standing them both back on the ground. "Only if you promise not to fall in."

"I won't," Andy assured him.

"But with any luck, perhaps *you* will," Reanna muttered under her breath. Immediately, she realized Travis had heard her. A guilty feeling niggled at her. Now why had she said that? It wasn't like her to be so waspish.

Travis must have wondered, too, for he glanced oddly at her, quirking a single eyebrow. "Good morning again, love. Did you miss me?"

"Of course not," she snapped, still ashamed of her derisive remark. Why was it that this particular man had the capacity to irritate her? And make her behave irrationally?

"Really?" He leaned nonchalantly against a nearby fence, studying her intently. "I must be slipping. Surely you missed me just a bit?"

"No, not at all," she insisted, wondering why she was participating in this ridiculous exchange. It was easy to tell he was playing with her. She met his glance and smiled.

"You've hardly given me reason to miss you. In fact, I'm delighted to be away from you."

"Well now." He pushed away from the fence, odd glints dancing in his eyes. "Is that another challenge, Reanna? I suppose I'll have to rectify that situation."

Before she realized his intention, he had swept her into his arms and was kissing her. His lips claimed hers, moving over her mouth commandingly. As the embrace deepened and demanded, Reanna felt her entire body flush with unexpected heat. She pulled away quickly. To her annoyance, she realized she was trembling. Why had he done that? They didn't need to pretend with the children.

"Aw, gee whiz," Andy said, "are you guys gonna do all that dumb mushy stuff?"

Her son's comment fueled Reanna's embarrassment. Her face burned hotly, particularly since Jenny and Andy were giggling.

"They're in love," Jenny said matter-of-factly. "They gotta do it."

"It's downright disgusting, isn't it, Andy?" David broke in, walking toward them. He was holding a bridle and grinning.

"Sure is," Andy agreed.

"Some day, young man, you'll disagree with that statement." Travis had reached to pull Reanna close. His arm encircled her possessively, and he smiled down at her. "Isn't that right, darling?"

"Yes, that's right," Reanna answered, forcing an answering smile. This was silly. She had to get hold of herself. Travis was purposely trying to disconcert her. And he was succeeding. He was the most maddening man she had ever met. And it had been the surprise that caused her reaction to his embrace. She hadn't anticipated his kiss, and she had been caught off guard. There was simply no other explanation for those tiny chills of awareness that had traversed her spine, and for her heart having started to thud at breakneck speed. It had to be the surprise.

Yet if he continued this charade, how was she ever going to get through the week? And more important, how was she going to get through several months of marriage?

CHAPTER FIVE

FRIDAY DAWNED WITH spectacular sunshine. It would be more fitting, Reanna thought as she pushed aside the bedroom curtains, if it were storming outside. At least the weather would match her mood—black and overcast. This was the final reckoning, and she dreaded it. All week, she had felt as though she were riding an emotional seesaw, one moment furious and the next strangely complacent. Travis had continued playing the charade; in public acting as though they were deeply in love, in private churlish and sarcastic, making innuendoes. It was confusing and bewildering. She didn't know how to act or what to say.

She leaned her head against the windowpane. Looking down into the garden where in less than an hour she would become Mrs. Travis Martin, she felt a cold knot of fear curl in her abdomen. She was marrying a stranger—a stranger from the past. Was she doing the right thing? It seemed wrong to marry without love—to marry a man she didn't trust, a man who held only hatred and distrust for her.

But it was a little late to back out now. All the preparations had been made. Thelma Mackey had worked feverishly all week. It was a beautiful scene. Chairs, strung together with wide, flower-bedecked ribbons, were set up in rows, and a wide velvet runner led to the canopy of flowers where she would take her vows. Fancy serving dishes had been placed on the lace-covered tables, awaiting the food, and at one end of the garden, adjacent to the softly flowing fountain, several musicians were tuning their instruments. No expense had been spared. This *was* the wedding of the century, Reanna realized when she noticed several reporters circulating among the guests who had already started arriving.

Beautifully dressed ladies and tuxedoed gentlemen walked under the giant oaks and willow trees, drinking mint juleps and chatting. A few couples sat on the white wrought-iron furniture, and others wandered through the garden near the fountain. Their gay laughter floated through the air to Reanna. Everyone seemed so happy— everyone except her. God help her, how was she going to get through this? She felt like a mass of quivering jelly.

Reanna turned to the mirror and ran her hands over the light peach-colored gown she was wearing. She had deliberated for hours over paying such a high price, but in the end had finally purchased it. She had to look decent on her wedding day, and the chiffon dress was perfect. It was plain, the neck slightly scooped and sewn with matching satin ribbon. Around her waist was another satin ribbon, which separated the fitted bodice from the softly swirling skirt, which ended just below her knees. She wore matching shoes, high-heeled sandals that accentuated her long legs—legs that were shaking.

Brides were usually nervous on their wedding day, but would anyone notice how uncommonly flushed she was? She literally glowed. For the third time, she powdered her face. If she wasn't careful, she would be able to peel off the makeup. She took a deep breath and, after brushing her hair for the umpteenth time, added a wide-brimmed straw hat. She looked like a typical southern belle, she thought, as she clutched the bouquet of baby's breath, wisteria, and tiny peach-colored rosebuds in her icy hands. Now, if she only felt like one . . .

A knock on her door startled her. She jumped and

whirled around. Her voice trembled as she said, "Come in."

"Reanna, you look lovely." It was Mr. Martin, dapper in a white tuxedo decorated with a tiny spray of flowers. Again Thelma Mackey's touch, Reanna suspected.

"Thank you." She stood staring at him.

"Are you nervous, dear?"

She laughed. "Whatever gives you that idea?"

"If you keep clutching those flowers so tightly, they're going to be crushed before you get downstairs."

"Oh." She placed the bouquet aside and removed her hat. She still had several minutes before she had to make the descent into hell. What would she do with her hands now? "I guess I am nervous."

"A typical bride," he said, beaming at her. "I've brought you something. You know that old saying, something old, something new, something borrowed, something blue? Well, these are old, they belonged to my wife."

He held out a strand of pearls. Reanna looked at them, awed. They were beautiful, long, each pearl the exact same size, tied individually. "Mr. Martin, they're lovely."

He placed the necklace in her hand. "I could never work the clasp, you'll have to put them on."

"But I can't accept these," Reanna objected, staring at them. "They're an heirloom."

"That's just the point, they're yours. As Travis's wife you should have them now. It's a family tradition to hand them down to the wife of the eldest son."

"Mr. Martin, I'm not—" She looked up at him, appealing to him to understand. What would Travis think if she accepted these pearls? Unfortunately, she knew the answer to that. But she could hardly point that out to the old man. Travis was his son. "One day Travis will marry someone who should have these . . . I . . . Travis and I . . . This marriage is just for—"

"I would like for you to have them, Reanna," he interrupted. "Please accept them, if only to make an old man happy. And I want you to wear them at the wedding for luck. You don't have something old, do you?"

He was superstitious, she had learned over the months. And so was Thelma, who had arranged for the tiny blue flowers that were weaved into her bouquet. Between the two of them, they had come up with so many traditions, it was mind-boggling.

"Perhaps I can borrow them," she said. "I don't have something borrowed, either."

"Well, we can easily fix that." He handed her a small white Bible. "Thelma wants you to use this. She carried it at her wedding. She said to place it under your bouquet, for more luck."

Reanna looked at the Bible through tear-blurred eyes. What a beautiful gesture. If only they realized that this wedding was a sham. "Thank you," she murmured.

"You'll wear the pearls, too?"

She couldn't disappoint him, but she couldn't accept the necklace, either. She looked at him with a pleading expression.

"Reanna," he said softly, "this strand of pearls is with their rightful owner. Traditionally, they will go to Andy's wife."

Andy was only four years old, a little young to be thinking of a wife, but Reanna nodded, understanding what he was saying. Perhaps she wasn't going to be Travis's wife in the true sense of the word, but Andy was still his son. "I'll take good care of them," she murmured, forcing her lips into a tight smile. "Thank you."

"Thank *you*, Reanna," Mr. Martin said. "Will you be all right?"

Although she wasn't certain, she nodded her affirmation.

* * *

Less than a half hour later, she was even less certain of her state of well-being. There was no putting it off any longer. She had waited until the last moment to come downstairs, but now she was poised on the threshold of the terrace doors.

Poised on the threshold of a new life. If only that were true.

It was time. Apparently, nothing was going to prevent this marriage. Neither of them had backed out; she was too strong to faint, and a knight on a white horse wasn't going to rescue her. On cue, the orchestra started to play the soft strains of the wedding march.

Wanting to flee in the opposite direction, Reanna took a deep breath and stepped out into the sunshine. Immediately, a low murmur shot through the crowd. Some of the guests were seeing her for the first time, she realized, and there had probably been a great deal of speculation about the woman who was becoming Mrs. Travis Martin. Now she was glad she had spent so much money on her dress. At least she looked her best.

"Oh, Aunt Reanna!" Jenny said, rushing to her side. She held a basket of rose petals, spilling most of them in her haste. "You're beautiful."

"And so are you," Reanna replied, automatically reaching to straighten the ribbon on Jenny's dress. It was made from the same material as her gown, but in a more child-like design. Aside from Marsha Prentiss, who was serving as Reanna's maid of honor, Jenny was her only attendant. She had wanted it that way. There was no one else she wanted to invite. Thelma and Mr. Martin had objected for days, but Reanna had remained adamant, refusing to give explanations. She could hardly invite her father—he had never forgiven her and never would, and she had no other family to speak of. To lose herself, she'd dropped contact with Shelly Robbins years ago.

"Are you ready?" Marsha Prentiss asked.

Reanna looked down the long aisle where Travis stood waiting with both his brothers. Involuntarily, her hands started to tremble. He looked so forbidding in his gray tuxedo, tall and long-legged, darkly handsome. "As ready as I'll ever be."

Jenny skipped ahead of her, strewing rose petals from the basket. All dressed up, too, was Andy. He sat squirming in a chair near the front, Mr. Martin at his side. Reanna smiled at him as she passed. He was her son, her life, worth any sacrifice.

"Hi, Mom," he said out loud. "Hurry up, okay? Gramps won't let me eat any cake till you get married. He doesn't want me to get dirty."

A smattering of laughter followed his statement. Reanna paused and kissed her son. How like Andy not to be awed by the proceedings. "Be a good boy," she whispered.

Then, with another deep breath, she continued down the aisle. God, what was she doing? It was too late, she kept repeating with each step—it was too late to run.

At the altar, she met Travis's gaze. Why did he have to look so cold and hostile? Why were his eyes so steely gray, so harsh and unrelenting? Trying hard not to waver, she smiled. One hand flitted up to finger the pearls, as though touching them could give her the courage she so desperately needed, and although she wasn't normally superstitious, a bit of luck, too.

"Shall we proceed?" the minister smiled kindly.

Taking her elbow, Travis gave a curt nod. "Go ahead."

The ceremony proceeded with Reanna in a daze. All she was aware of was Travis's warm hand enclosing her cold one, the sound of his husky voice repeating the wedding vows, the ring sliding on her finger. She repeated her vows, too, but she didn't even know what she said. Everything was a blur of sights and sounds, of suspended animation. She wasn't really getting married. This girl standing at the altar pledging eternal devotion wasn't Reanna Williamson. It was someone else, someone apart. Then, suddenly, it was over, and Travis was leaning down to kiss her.

Cameras whined in their faces as he turned her around to face the crowd. "Smile now," he murmured, leaning over to embrace her again for the benefit of the reporters. "If you have trouble, think about your pearls."

Reanna saw red, and it wasn't from the flashbulbs. Couldn't he let a single moment pass without making innuendoes and accusations? "For your information, your father gave me these."

"I didn't think you broke into the safe to steal them," he replied, still smiling at the cameras. "It didn't take you long to carry out your threat, did it?"

Reanna clenched her jaw to keep from exploding. He knew damned well she was being sarcastic that night. "Just what the hell are you suggesting?"

"Only the obvious, love." The pressure of his hand on hers increased in a warning. There were people watching. "Shall we greet our guests?"

They were promptly surrounded by the crowd, everyone anxious to offer congratulations. Travis kept her at his side, introducing her to hundreds of people, touching her, kissing her, until she thought she was going to go crazy. He was certainly charming, a master of the game. Although she didn't know how she accomplished it, she kept smiling.

Several hours passed while they held court to his family. Cousin Lucy was the only one she remembered, probably because they had talked about the woman before. Since it was the only thing Travis handed her, Reanna drank several glasses of punch. They danced, cut the cake and ate, and all the while Reanna felt numbed. Later, when Travis removed her garter to the bumping strains of stripping music, she flushed. It was all so intimate. It was all so fake.

By the time darkness descended, Reanna felt as though she couldn't endure another moment. Her feet ached, and her face hurt from smiling and chatting. Yet the party atmosphere prevailed. People were still dancing and celebrating. More bottles of champagne than she had ever seen in her life were opened and consumed. Jenny and Andy, both filthy and exhausted, were asleep on a sofa. She wanted to join them, but Cousin Lucy was beside her.

"You must be *so* excited," the woman was saying. "This is just like a fairy tale."

"Yes," Reanna responded politely.

"The governess gets the wealthy heir." She giggled. "And to think I never believed those romance novels."

Reanna frowned. For some reason, she didn't like the woman. As she recalled, Travis didn't like her, either, and for the first time, she agreed with him. "I'm not a governess, Cousin Lucy, and I didn't *get* Travis, I *married* him."

"Well, teacher. It's the same thing." Lucy shrugged her shoulders in an expansive gesture and continued, "But really, dear, you must tell me how you managed to trap my wonderful cousin. He's such a rake. Why, most of the female population in Lexington has been after him for years. Myself included. We're only distantly related, you know."

"No," Reanna said. "I didn't know."

Lucy giggled again, obviously drunk. "It doesn't matter now. That was when we were kids. Oh, how I loved him, but he was always with those smelly horses. Ugh. I hate horses. Did you know I'm getting married myself in September? To Tom. Now where is he?" She looked around the room as though just realizing she was missing her fiancé. "You must have already met him. He's the banker. He owns the biggest bank in Lexington."

"Oh," Reanna said.

"But really now, you must tell me how you ensnared Travis. And so quickly. Why, we had hardly realized you were working here, and then you were getting married. Was it love at first sight?"

"Something like that." Reanna bit her tongue to keep from being nasty. Her relationship with Travis wasn't Cousin Lucy's business. She wanted to tell her that, but she could hardly be rude to a guest.

"Lord, but he's a hunk. Whew! What a wedding night you're going to have!" Lucy's giggles were beginning to irritate Reanna. "I'll bet you can hardly wait to get him alone."

"Yes." Her smile felt frozen on her face. It was almost with a sense of relief that she spotted Travis in the crowd, heading toward her. Perhaps he would be kind enough to rescue her. She had a moment's concern, though, about the entourage of men following him. She was reminded of the Pied Piper, only these were adults.

"Pardon me, Cousin Lucy," Travis said, bowing formally to Reanna. "May I steal away my bride?"

To Reanna's absolute shock, he grinned and swept her up in his arms. "What are you doing? Put me down!" she hissed. She'd wanted to be rescued, not abducted.

"It's time for the finale, love."

That was exactly her concern. What was the finale? "Travis, I swear, if you embarrass me . . ."

"And what will you do, Reanna? Divorce me?"

Ignoring her objections, he had weaved his way through the guests, carrying her toward the circular staircase that led to the bedrooms.

"Will you please tell me what you're doing?" she demanded.

"You'll soon see," he murmured, pausing on the first step. "Just a bit of tradition."

She should have suspected something, but Reanna was shocked when he let her slide down his body and kissed her. This time it wasn't the chaste embrace they had shared at the ceremony, or the tiny kisses he had tortured her with throughout the reception, but a deep, sensuous clinch. His lips devoured hers, and his hands seemed to be everywhere at once, trailing along her back to cup her hips and thrust them against his, up into her hair to hold her firmly to him. She felt her breath coming in quick pants as she struggled against him. The crowd of drunken men cheered their approval.

"Very good, love," he whispered when his lips left hers. "In fact, that was excellent. You seemed so properly anxious."

"You know damned well I was struggling!" she said, her cheeks staining red. Adding to her chagrin, a chorus of whistles had greeted the end of the embrace.

Now David popped the cork on a champagne bottle. "To Travis and Reanna," he said, holding his glass high. "And to their heirs. May their sons be healthy and strong."

"And soon," Jonathan added.

Reanna wanted to die, right there on the spot. They may as well have given Travis some sort of ancient phallic symbol. But it wasn't over yet.

Travis took the glass of champagne David held out and drank from it. "Yes, and soon." He held it to her lips.

She almost choked. This was too much. They were going too far! Against her will, she took a sip. More cheers resounded when Travis carelessly flipped the empty glass against the stone floor, breaking the fragile crystal into a million shards. Before she had fully absorbed the significance of the gesture, he kissed her a second time—deep, probing, bending her body to his will. Then in one quick, fluid movement, he swept her into his arms again and started up the steps.

"Have fun, my boy!" someone shouted.

To hide the scarlet flush that seemed to have become her permanent complexion, Reanna buried her face in Travis's shoulder. Never, never had she felt so humiliated. In the past week, he'd embarrassed her, but this—this was the height of insult. Anger simmered inside her like hot oil in a caldron, only to increase to boiling when he kicked open the door to his room and slammed it behind them as though he were some pagan, carrying off his woman. She could still hear the cheers from downstairs.

Under ordinary circumstances, Reanna might have noticed the masculine overtones of the room. It was large, more like a studio than a bedroom, easily triple the size of hers. One wall was an entire window of doors that led onto a small terrace. Moonlight filtered through the gauzy draperies that fluttered in the slight breeze from the night air. A huge stone fireplace, surrounded by a small end table and chairs, dominated the room. The furnishings were of a rich, dark oak that shone with the luster of age. Everything hinted of heritage, the chifforobe, the long, deep bureau, the massive four-poster bed.

But nothing registered in Reanna's mind except her anger. Travis had deposited her unceremoniously on the floor and turned away, starting to strip off his tie.

"Damn you!" she choked, her voice barely discernible. She could hardly speak. "How dare you humiliate me!"

"Sorry, love, but that was part of the bargain."

For a moment, she *was* speechless. The audacity of this man! He was by far the most aggravating person she had ever met—smug, cynical, and overbearing. "How dare you! *How dare you!*"

He sighed. "That's the third time you've how-dared me.

Get to the point, Reanna. I'm tired, and I'm not in the mood for feminine hysterics."

Hysterics! Hysterics! It took a supreme effort, but she managed to calm herself so that she could speak. Each word was enunciated, drawn out. "Every person at that reception thinks that we're up here making love!"

Travis paused in the midst of unbuttoning the shirt of his tuxedo. He had tossed his cuff links carelessly onto the dresser. "That's what married people generally do on their wedding night."

"They don't do it in their room while several hundred people are downstairs!" she shouted. "And we are not ordinary married people!"

"Lower your voice, Reanna." He turned back to her so swiftly it made her dizzy. "It's a bit early to be developing our irreconcilable differences."

Beyond reason, she whirled to leave. She'd be damned if she'd stay here, marriage or no marriage.

"Where the hell do you think you're going?"

Something in his tone made her halt, some aura of command. She glared at him defiantly, her hand poised on the doorknob. "To my room."

"In case you haven't noticed, my sweet," he said, spreading his arm out in a grand gesture, "you're already there. This is your room."

Reanna dug her heels in stubbornly. "I won't stay here. I refuse to share your room."

"As I recall, you don't have a choice. We are married, remember?" Their gazes, clashing together, fought a silent battle. Then Travis sighed. "Look, it's been a long day. We're both tired, and this argument isn't serving any purpose. Why don't we go to bed?"

She blinked in disbelief. Surely he didn't expect her to sleep with him! "Might I ask just where you expect me to sleep? In case *you* haven't noticed, that is a double bed."

"It's a king-sized bed," he corrected.

"That's hardly the issue," she grated out.

"True." His mock patience was infuriating. He was treating her as though she were a child in the throes of a temper tantrum. "To be perfectly honest, Reanna, I don't care where you sleep. If you wish, you may use the floor, or the chairs, or the dresser, or the bed. Or you can stand there all night, but you will stay in this room and you will lower your voice, if for nothing more than Andy's sake. Now, if you'll excuse me, I intend to get some sleep."

Clearly, she was dismissed. It galled her, but more aggravating, once again he was right. This pretense was necessary for Andy. In anger, she'd lost sight of that fact. Trying to control her turbulent emotions, she started to fiddle with the pearls at her neck. She had forgotten them, too. She reached up to remove them and stood immobile until Travis turned back to her. Without a word, she placed them on his dresser.

"What about the ring?" he asked sarcastically. "Are you going to return it, too?"

For the first time, she looked at the heavy ring he had placed on her finger. It was an antique like the necklace, a very expensive heirloom. Several large diamonds glittered from a thick band of gold. She started to remove it, but Travis laughed harshly.

"Don't bother for now, Reanna. Just don't hock it."

She clenched her jaw to keep from retorting. She was tired of arguing. She looked around in indecision. What should she do? Even if she wanted to go to bed, was she supposed to sleep in her clothes?

As if reading her mind, he turned back to her. "Thelma moved your things during the reception. Your clothes are in the chifforobe."

When had they planned that? It seemed that every person in this house was plotting against her. Thelma, Mr.

Martin, David, Jonathan—they were all making this more difficult than she'd anticipated.

"She was trying to be thoughtful. You do remember that we're supposed to be in love?" He swept a froth of white material off the end of the bed and tossed it to her. "More thoughtfulness."

Reanna caught the filmy garment in her hand. It was lovely—a long, sheer gown of the finest silk, with a tiny blue ribbon threaded through the deep-plunging bodice. She flushed at the implication. Thoughtful or no, did he really expect her to wear it?

"The bathroom's through that door."

Evidently, he did. But Reanna had her own plan in mind. If she had to sleep in the same room with Travis, it certainly wasn't going to be in a seductive nightgown. Perhaps she was acting infantile, but if she was being treated that way, why not behave accordingly? She tossed the gown aside and went to the chifforobe, rummaging through the lower drawers. When Andy had been born and she had been up late at night nursing him, she'd invested in one or two warm flannel gowns. Well worn and comfortable, they covered her from head to toe. For one fleeting moment, she thought about the temperature outside. This was the middle of summer. She would roast in a flannel gown.

Oh well. Where Travis Martin was concerned, her stubbornness outweighed her better judgment. Clutching one of the warm gowns, Reanna slammed the door of the bathroom behind her. She stripped quickly and tossed the garment over her head, buttoning it to her throat. Even her toothbrush had been moved, she discovered. It was perched beside Travis's inside the medicine chest. Thelma had been thorough in transferring Reanna's belongings, right down to the cold cream she used to remove her makeup.

Suddenly, a smug smile curved her lips. Were her

curlers here, too? Her hair was naturally curly, but she had bought the rollers when she was a teenager, and hadn't parted with them. That was one of her bad habits—she kept everything.

Reanna slammed the door again when she exited the bathroom. Again, childish, but she wanted to bring attention to herself. Between the white cream, heavily coated on her face and the brush rollers that stuck from her hair at odd angles, she knew she must look like an alien from outer space. A thrill of satisfaction rippled through her when Travis looked up.

He was lying in bed, sipping at a glass of dark amber liquid. A short dressing robe in a deep wine color covered his body, sashed at the waist. The open neck revealed a smattering of thick, dark hair that curled over his broad chest. For a moment, Reanna thought his jaw was going to drop open in disbelief, but then he seemed to stifle a smile. Just as quickly, the humor also disappeared.

"Let's get something perfectly clear, Reanna," he said, slowly placing the glass aside and rising from the bed. "I have no desire whatsoever to consummate this marriage. It may surprise you to know that despite what happened between us five years ago, I have no inclination to make love to you. As far as I'm concerned, you could strip nude and it wouldn't disturb me."

As he spoke, he advanced on her. Reanna felt like a cornered animal. Her limbs seemed paralyzed by his intent gaze, and her heart started to thud at breakneck speed.

"But if I did want to make love to you"—he ran his finger along her cheek, making an indentation in the thick cold cream—"this would hardly deter me."

It all happened at once: his arms surrounding her roughly, his fingers wrapping tightly in her long hair, the curlers scattering onto the floor, his lips hard and demanding on hers. The embrace was so intense it took her breath away. As he clutched her to his body, his mouth was warm, tasting slightly of Scotch, and yet at the same time felt slippery from the cream. The combination was oddly sensuous. Although she struggled, a strange tingling began deep in her loins, racing featherlike along her thighs, up into her stomach to curl in a tight knot—of what? All she knew was that it was like an unleashed fire smoldering within her.

She didn't have time to examine the sensation, for Travis abruptly released her and walked away. She stood there for several long, humiliating moments. Had he known? Had he guessed? She'd been devastated by that kiss.

"Good night, Reanna." He switched off the light.

Still standing immobile, she touched her lips with one hand. They felt bruised and swollen and very thoroughly kissed. More to the point, they felt *delightfully* bruised and swollen and very thoroughly kissed. Her heart was still beating at triphammer speed, and her breath was coming in short, rapid gasps. It had aroused her; the embrace had aroused her. She had wanted him. There was no denying it. For one brief moment, she had wanted him. Self-disgust consumed her, washing over her in waves. What kind of woman was she?

Slowly, forcing her trembling limbs to comply, she walked to a chair and sat down. The terrace windows were to her right. Illuminated by moonlight, the Martin estate stretched as far as she could see—gentle rolling hills, long, dark expanses of grass, a few horses grazing peacefully in the pasture. From downstairs she could still hear the sounds of celebration—her marriage celebration.

Reanna closed her eyes and swallowed the lump of emotion that rose in her throat. She would not cry. She would not allow herself to cry! She tilted her chin high and stared out the windows for the longest time, all the while fingering the gold ring on her left hand.

It was dawn when Travis gave up trying to sleep and got out of bed. Reanna was still in the chair, sound asleep, her head tilted to one side. Her eyes were puffy, as though she'd been crying, and there were still traces of cold cream on her face. She was perspiring, too, with that impossible nightgown buttoned all the way to her neck. Where in the world had she gotten such an ugly thing? It had little yellow vines on it and tiny lace stitched along the hem and sleeves. She looked so damned innocent. She'd taken in his father and his brothers and even Thelma Mackey. They all adored her.

Was there a possibility he was wrong about her? It had surprised him when she gave back the necklace. It was worth a fortune. As though he could guess her designs from her face in repose, he studied her intently. She was stubborn, too—the most stubborn woman he'd ever met. She'd slept in that chair all night, and she was going to have one hell of a backache this morning. Not knowing quite why, he gathered her in his arms. She roused slightly, but when he placed her on the bed, she snuggled against the pillow and sighed. A sudden rush of emotion made him want to brush the hair from her cheek and tuck in the covers.

Steeling himself to the strange protectiveness that tugged at him, Travis turned away and continued dressing. Looks were deceiving, particularly with a woman like Reanna. Just before he left the room, he glanced at her again. Then, abruptly, he went back to the dresser and tossed the pearls onto the chifforobe. What the hell. She deserved something for her troubles.

CHAPTER SIX

REANNA WAS DISORIENTED WHEN she woke up. Everything registered at once: the bright sunlight streaming through the windows, the unfamiliar surroundings. This was Travis's room, his bed. And she was lying in it. The last thing she remembered was drifting off to sleep in the chair. How had she gotten into the bed? More importantly, was he beside her? Were they sleeping together? The thought alarmed her. She was a heavy sleeper and had a tendency to sprawl over the bed. She lay still several long moments, hardly daring to breathe.

It was with a sense of relief that she realized she was alone. Travis was gone. At least she would be able to dress in private. She had to think about this situation. When she'd agreed to marry him, she hadn't considered the more intimate things they would be forced to share—like a room and a bed. First and foremost, she had to find a place to sleep. The crick in her neck ached unbearably. There was grease all over her hair as well, and she felt hot and sticky from wearing the flannel gown.

For the moment, though, finding a solution to her dilemma could wait. Irrationally deciding she could face anything after a shower, Reanna slipped into the bathroom and let the hot water pound on her for endless minutes. She soaped herself from head to toe, relishing the sharp needles that riddled her skin. Feeling almost human again, she toweled herself dry and went to find a pair of jeans. It was late. She had to get downstairs. Jenny and Andy were

probably bothering Thelma, who was more than likely trying to clean up from last night.

As she opened the doors to the chifforobe, the pearls
tumbled to the floor. Frowning, Reanna picked them up
and stared at them. Travis must have placed them there.
She distinctly remembered putting them on his dresser.
What an odd thing for him to do. Did he intend for her to
have them? And if he did, why?

There weren't any logical answers to her questions. Not
bothering to ponder his curious action any longer, Reanna
placed the necklace on the shelf and pulled out an old shirt,
hurriedly dressing. She would make a point of returning
the pearls later. Whatever his reasons, there were two
things she was certain of: She would not sleep with Travis
Martin, and she didn't want a single item that came from
him.

As it turned out, Jenny and Andy weren't bothering
Thelma at all. They weren't anywhere in sight. In fact, no
one seemed to be in the house. The silence was the first
thing that struck her. Surely everyone couldn't still be
asleep?

"Thelma?" Reanna called, pushing open the kitchen
door.

The housekeeper was in the midst of reshining a
countertop. She must have gotten up at dawn. There were
no remaining traces of yesterday's reception. From the
looks of things, the whole wedding could have been merely
a dream. Reanna wished it had been.

"Good morning." Thelma smiled at her. There were a
thousand unspoken questions in her expression. "You're
looking mighty chipper today. Did you sleep well?"

Reanna paused and cleared her throat, only now realizing how difficult it was going to be facing people. "Yes,
thank you."

"Mister Travis was up early," Thelma went on. "We

thought he would sleep in, too. Sure was a surprise to see him at breakfast. He said not to disturb you, that you were awfully tired."

It didn't take much imagination to guess what he'd intimated. Despite herself, Reanna flushed. She wondered if she would feel as awkward under different circumstances. "That was kind of him. Thank you for the nightgown, Thelma. It's very beautiful."

The woman literally beamed. A slight flush spotted her face, too, and she started to fidget with a pot. "You're welcome." Her voice lowered conspiratorially. "Mister Travis thanked me, too, but he said you didn't use it much."

Did he now? Ordinarily, Reanna would have been angry at that, but recalling his look at the gown she *had* worn, she had to stifle a grin. "No, I didn't," she answered honestly, "but it's still beautiful, and I appreciate the gesture."

Thelma continued to fuss at the stove, and her blush had deepened. She was clearly embarrassed by her own curiosity. For the first time, she seemed at a loss for words.

"Well, if you'll excuse me now," Reanna said, "I need to find the children."

The housekeeper looked up, obviously thankful at the change in subject. "Oh, Jenny and Andy are out picking blueberries with Mister Charles. I'm going to make a pie for dessert tonight; nothing like fresh blueberries, you know, for taste. I'm a bit worried about Mister Charles, though, tramping through the woods with those little ones. He has arthritis, you know."

"I'll go find them," Reanna assured her, but she never made it outside. She was walking out the front door when Travis came in. For a moment, she stood speechless. What should she say to him? Should she confront him with his innuendoes to Thelma? She felt incongruously shy and reticent. Then she noticed his expression.

"Reanna."

It was a single word, and for some reason it frightened her. Instinctively, she realized something had happened. Something was wrong. She searched his face, her stomach lurching in fear. What was it?

"Reanna," he said again. softly. "I don't know how to tell you this, but your father is in the hospital in Louisville. He's had a heart attack."

She thought the earth had been pulled from beneath her. It wasn't possible. Not her father! He was never sick. Les Williamson was invincible. This was a joke, a cruel joke. For some reason, Travis was lying to her. Deep down inside, she knew that wasn't true. It was just that the situation was so unbelievable. Yet that wasn't the truth, either. She had known that one day something like this would happen. Her father had that heart condition, and he smoked. Suddenly, the room started spinning. Her knees buckled.

Reanna felt Travis's arms on hers, holding her up, and she heard him, but she couldn't command her body to function further. Everything was a blur.

"He was admitted this morning. The doctor happened to see the newspaper reports of our wedding and called me." Gently, he told her, "Reanna, he's in Intensive Care. He wants to see you."

"Andy?" It was all she could say.

"Don't worry about Andy. Thelma and my father can take care of him. Come. Let's get your things. We have to hurry."

Reanna didn't remember packing. She felt so alone—so utterly alone, and shattered, like one of those fragile crystal figurines that had been crushed into millions of fragments by a breath of wind. A ship, perhaps, full-masted, or a soaring bird.

While she sat on the bed, stunned, Thelma and Travis

stuffed her clothing into a suitcase. She went to the chif-forobe once, but couldn't remember what it was that she'd wanted.

She didn't recall much of the trip to Louisville, either. It didn't occur to her to question why Travis was beside her, driving her to her father's bedside—or to ponder his concerned expression. Everything was happening too quickly: the coincidence of coming here to Martin Oaks, her marriage to Travis, her father's illness. Why now? Why had the fates heaped all this misery on her at once?

And why had she been so damned stubborn? All she could think of was that her father might die. At the hospital, just before they got out of the car, Travis took her hand.

Together they walked inside. At the entrance to the Intensive Care unit, he paused. "Reanna, stay here while I let them know we've arrived."

She nodded, staring at the huge doors in front of them. Moments later, he returned with a doctor at his side.

"Mrs. Martin?"

Who was that? She frowned. Of course, that was her. She was Mrs. Martin.

"Your father has had an acute myocardial infarction. He's very weak. I'm going to be honest with you, I'm not certain he's going to pull out of this. He's a stubborn man, though, and that may work in his favor."

Yes, her father was stubborn. So was she. Those doors were so forbidding. What would she find on the other side?

"He's been asking for you since he was admitted. When you go in, please don't say anything to tax him. If he doesn't answer, please realize he's been sedated."

Again she nodded, walking toward the doors. Her father was weak. He had been sedated. But nothing the doctor could have told her would have prepared her for the sight of him. Les Williamson had so many tubes strung into his body that Reanna couldn't count them all. He was as pale as the white sheet that was tucked over his chest, his thick red hair a shock of stark color. Beads of perspiration dampened his forehead; oxygen infused into his nose. Above, a monitor registered his heartbeat. To the side, another machine pumped fluid into his body. A respirator was nearby.

Reanna sat in the chair at his bedside. Travis stood behind her, his hand on her shoulder at first hesitant, then solid, offering her strength and reassurance.

"Daddy," she whispered.

Les Williamson's eyes fluttered open for the briefest moment. The blue pupils were cloudy, remote. "Reanna?"

"Yes, Daddy, it's me." She took his hand.

It seemed to require sheer strength of will for him to open his eyes again. When he spoke, it was an utterance of relief. "Reanna."

"Don't talk, Daddy," she said. "Don't tire yourself out. The doctor says you mustn't waste your strength."

Her father nodded, but he continued, even though each word was an effort that robbed him of life. "I want to know . . . the baby?"

"Andy?" she asked, fighting back tears. She couldn't cry; not here, not now. "Andy is fine."

"A boy?"

"Yes, he's a darling little boy."

"My father." His words were getting garbled, but Reanna understood. She had named Andy after her paternal grandfather. "What . . . what does he look like?"

"He has blond hair and blue eyes." She laughed, but it wasn't all from humor. "I think his hair is turning a bit red, now, like yours, and he has a terrible temper."

Les Williamson smiled wanly. "A devil, huh?"

Reanna fumbled in her purse. "Yes, he's a devil, all right. I have a photograph. Would you like to keep it?"

The nod was barely discernible. From above, the monitor began to sound an alarm.

"Mr. Martin, Mrs. Martin, I'm afraid you'll have to go now," a nurse told them softly. "Mr. Williamson's heart rate is increasing. We don't want him to become too excited."

Travis nodded, gently pulling Reanna up. "Come, Reanna, your father needs to rest."

She paused, torn between wanting to stay at her father's side and doing the right thing. "Daddy, I have to leave now, but I'll be here. I'll be right outside. I'll visit you some more in just a little while."

Les Williamson didn't answer. Each breath was a labored gasp, but he clutched the picture of his grandson in his hand.

Gently, Travis led Reanna to the waiting room. For a moment, neither of them spoke. Then Travis sighed. "Would you like some coffee?"

"No." She stared at him through unseeing eyes.

"Reanna, let me get you something. How about tea?"

She shook her head again. "No, nothing, thank you."

Time had no meaning for her. She sat there for hours, but it could have been days, or even weeks, or perhaps moments. It was all the same. Travis clasped her hand in his, his warm gesture giving her much-needed courage.

The next time she visited her father, she held his hand tightly, as though she could infuse life by her touch—as though she could transfer the sustenance Travis gave her. For Travis had given her the ability to survive. She wasn't certain when she'd started to depend on him for support. Perhaps it was when he'd clasped her hand in the car, perhaps when he'd grasped her shoulder at her father's bedside. All she knew was that he had become her lifeline.

But no matter what she did, Les Williamson seemed to grow weaker and weaker. The monitor sounded the alarm over and over. Nurses changed shifts, doctors came and went, speaking to her in hushed tones. Reanna prayed for strength, for guidance, for forgiveness. Through it all, Travis remained at her side. When she was frightened, watching the emergency team rush into the Intensive Care unit and back out, shaking their heads, he held her tightly. When she paced the floor, he led her to a chair.

"Here, Reanna, have some soup." He held the spoon to her lips, his solicitude a sharp contrast to a few days ago, when he had tried to embarrass her. "You need to keep up your strength."

She did as he asked, because he asked. And she didn't cry. Her father wouldn't want her to cry.

"Such a shame." Two nurses were passing by. "And on their honeymoon, too."

"Mr. Martin, I'm from the business office. I didn't want to disturb your wife . . ." Soft murmurs. "I'm so sorry."

"We're doing everything we can." This time it was a doctor. "She needs some rest. She's exhausted. Take her somewhere. Just leave us a telephone number."

Reanna didn't want to go, but Travis was insistent. She was surprised to see the gray shards of dawn break the sky. Where had the night gone?

They checked into a hotel. Still in an exhausted trance, unaware of her nudity, she undressed, right there in front of him.

"Travis." She turned, staring at him through tear-blurred eyes. "What if he dies? What if my father dies?"

"He's not going to die, Reanna," Travis said, holding her shoulders in a firm grip. Then, without hesitation, he enfolded her in his arms. The tears came, slowly at first, then in giant sobbing gasps. He patted her, comforting her like a child. "It's going to be all right, Reanna. Believe me, everything's going to be fine."

She believed him; she believed in him. When he placed

her ever so gently on the bed and stretched beside her, holding her tenderly, sweeping back her hair, she didn't object. Miraculously, she slept.

That night, when they returned to the hospital, her father was still weak, but his color was better. The nurses weren't hovering over him. Reanna felt a thrill of relief. Travis was right. Her father was going to recover. She looked up at her husband as she held her father's hand. He nodded, a silent communication.

"Travis?" Her father's voice was raspy, puzzled. "Travis Martin? Is that you?"

"Hello, Les. What are you trying to do, get out of racing your colt against me?"

"Commander can beat that nag of yours in a walk. You got yourself a gray jinx, Martin."

"Think you can scare me with that old superstition? Get out of that bed and prove it."

"Don't worry, you won't walk on my grave. We'll see you in the Derby, if not before." He slept then. And the next time he awoke he was stronger. Reanna was alone with him, for Travis was talking to David on the phone.

Les touched the ring on her finger. "Who?"

"Travis. We were married last week."

"Andy's father?"

Was he asking for affirmation or information? How much did he remember? "Yes," Reanna whispered. Would he understand what she was saying?

"Should have told me. He's a good man . . . good horseman."

Perhaps he did understand.

By the third day, Les Williamson was much, much stronger. When Reanna walked into his room, he was shouting at the nurses and bucking authority. "Daddy, please calm down," she said, glancing sympathetically at the flushed nurse.

"Calm down? I've got a horse to train. And what are you doing here? Travis has a horse to train, too. And who's with Andy? You should be home, young lady, minding your marriage."

Two days later, she did leave, just to make her father happy. So what if she had to drive back and forth several days a week to visit? She'd be home, where she belonged, not at the hospital hovering over him. At his insistence, her father had been moved out of Intensive Care, into a surveillance unit. He would have a long recuperation, but the doctors were optimistic. They'd been startled at his recovery, and more startled at his brusque, no-nonsense attitude. Les Williamson was determined to beat the odds.

Travis was silent on the way home, and Reanna didn't know how to broach a subject other than her father's illness. The closer they got to Martin Oaks, the more anxious she felt. What would they do now? How would they act toward each other? Would they go back to their cutting animosity? While Travis had been tender and supportive, he hadn't spoken to her since they'd left the hospital. Confused, she twisted her wedding ring around and around on her finger. It surprised her to realize she missed Travis's hand on hers, his husky voice soothing her. It was silly of her to think he'd meant more than sympathy by those touches. Had she thought that? What had she thought? She was so mixed up.

"Reanna?"

Travis had tried to concentrate on the road, but he kept watching Reanna twist her wedding ring around on her finger. He'd been thinking hard, and wondered if he hadn't misjudged her. There didn't seem to be any pretense now. She'd been devastated by her father's heart attack. Personally, for more reasons than he cared to admit, he was glad the ordeal was over and that they were going home. The past few days of holding her in his arms had been living hell. Whenever he was around her, his body reacted like a teenager's, burgeoning with hormones. All he could think of was of making love to her. Those nights they had slept together with her wearing that sheer nightgown had been pure torture.

"Reanna," he called again, wanting to apologize to her for his former suspicions. It was the least he could do.

"Yes?" She jumped and snapped her purse closed. She'd been searching for a tissue and hadn't meant to react so violently, but she had been startled by his harsh tone.

There was a long, awkward silence while Travis flicked his gaze back to the road. A dark frown knitted his brow. For a moment, he was certain he'd seen the pearls in her purse. It was hard to believe that she had remembered them in the midst of a crisis. Were they that important to her? Perhaps he wasn't wrong about her, after all. "Never mind," he muttered, "we're almost home."

"Yes." Reanna couldn't help but wonder what he'd been about to say, and what had happened to destroy their new-found rapport. Travis was clearly angry about something. What had she done to upset him? The past five days, he had been tender, gentle, caring . . . and now, suddenly, he was brusque and ill-tempered. Tucking her purse on her lap, she turned to the window and sighed. Travis Martin's mood swings were beyond her comprehension. Never, never would she be able to figure out this moody man she had married.

CHAPTER SEVEN

FOR THE REMAINDER of the ride, Travis didn't speak again, and neither did Reanna. She looked out the car window at the famous bluegrass, at the romping horses in pasture after endless pasture. This was horse country—the undisputed capital of Thoroughbred racing.

It was a beautiful, genteel atmosphere, but beyond those rolling meadows was the labor of dedicated horsemen that gave Kentucky its heritage. Training for a Thoroughbred started at birth. To simplify records, a horse attained age by the calendar. January first was the birthday of all foals, no matter when during the calendar year they were born. Soon after, the animal was petted, fondled, and spoken to, until the touch of a human hand and the sound of a voice were second nature. Even frolicking was work for a newborn horse. To teach discipline and to avoid injury, the animal was haltered and required to walk behind its mother into the pasture. Over and over, the task was repeated.

Then, on the horse's first birthday, serious work began. Saddles and bridles, riders, lead lines, starting gates, noises, various track conditions—all the things a horse had to learn were gradually introduced. Strengths and weaknesses were evaluated until, at age two, the animal faced its first trial—a race.

Such a fragile animal, the Thoroughbred horse, and so young for such a challenge. Adulthood wasn't attained for several more years, and still, they raced, and gave, and gave some more. Speed and stamina were inbred. Inside, if the animal was a champion, beat a heart that defied defeat. Yet so many things could happen in a race. Over one thousand pounds of muscle, sinew, and bone were supported on tiny, spindly legs. Hitting the turf with thousands of pounds of tension, bones were easily shattered. Lungs could start to hemorrhage; sickness and death could occur if extreme care wasn't exercised. Twenty-four hours a day the Thoroughbred required scrupulous attention.

Reanna had loved every moment she spent training horses. She missed it now—the excitement, the thrill of winning when you were the person responsible for the molding of a champion, even the disappointments. She glanced at Travis, studying the clean lines of his face, the solid thrust of his jaw. Did he feel that way? Yes, he was a horseman in every sense of the word, dedicated, stubborn, strong, undaunted in the face of adversity.

"Is something wrong?"

She sighed. Everything was wrong. If she could only define it, pinpoint what was disturbing her. "No."

"We're home." Travis seemed disturbed, too. Distracted, that was the word. His expression was remote as he opened the car door. Then, after greeting his father and Andy, he went directly to the stables.

"Where's Jenny?" Reanna asked.

"With Mrs. Webber," Andy supplied, hugging her again. Chocolate syrup covered his face, and he smeared it all over Reanna. "She's studying."

Mr. Martin smiled. "I hope you don't mind, dear. We had to hire someone. We didn't know when you would be back, and Jonathan didn't want Jenny to lose time with her studies."

"Oh." Reanna felt strangely hurt. She would miss working with Jenny.

"And then, too, it doesn't seem appropriate for you to continue with Jenny now that you're married to Travis.

Mrs. Webber is very qualified . . . and we had to do something."

"That's fine, Mr. Martin. I understand." What would she do for money now? She'd depended on her salary. Being Travis's wife was hardly a source of income.

"How is your father?"

"As obstinate as ever." She laughed, for the moment pushing her concerns aside. She would manage somehow. She always did. "When we left, he was telling the nurses he wasn't about to have a bath in bed. He wasn't an invalid. He had horses to train. Why couldn't they understand that?"

Mr. Martin nodded heartily. "Good. I understand Travis invited your father here to recuperate. I want you to know I second that invitation, but Les has to leave Commander at the track. That colt might beat us."

Reanna was surprised by Travis's considerate gesture, yet she was puzzled as well. She thought about it as she ascended the steps to their bedroom. Why would he do something like that—to offer his home to her father, particularly when he suspected she was after his money? It didn't make sense. But then, the entire situation didn't make sense.

She showered, washing off the chocolate syrup, and pulled out an old shirt. Then, on sudden impulse, she replaced the garment and reached for a brightly patterned full skirt in hues of blue. Along with a peasant blouse in soft white cotton, it would be cool and comfortable in the summer heat. She applied a light dusting of blush and dabbed on pale lipstick. Appearances, she told herself as she pulled her hair back and cinched it with a ribbon. The care she was taking with her attire had nothing to do with the possibility of seeing Travis.

Thelma was dusting furniture in the foyer when she came back downstairs. "Oh, Miss Reanna, it's so good to have you back." The housekeeper beamed. "And I hear your father is going to be just fine. I'll be fixing up a room for him right away. We want to be prepared, you know."

"Thank you, Thelma," Reanna replied, smiling fondly. "Would you happen to know where Andy got to?"

"I hate to mention this with you just getting back from your father being sick and all, but Master Andy is with Mister Charles at the stable. I don't know what's happened to Mister Charles these days. I think he's going to let Mister Andy have one of those kittens in the house, and Miss Jenny's allergic to cats, you know, and all that hair—"

"I'll take care of it, Thelma," Reanna said.

Shaking her head in amusement, she headed for the stables in search of her son. Thelma would never change. Reanna was nearly at the barns when she noticed Travis was standing beside a fence, watching Scimitar work out. The colt was breezing, but giving his rider a bad time by bucking and lurching at the rail.

Not wanting to interrupt the training session, she leaned against the fence, just watching. It was easy to understand what Travis saw in the animal. In stride, the horse was poetry in motion—smooth, fluid, his big muscles bunching, his forelegs stretching out in a ground-eating gallop. If he were better behaved, he might be a winner.

"Bring him in, David," Travis shouted when Scimitar lurched again. Clearly disgusted, he whirled around.

The force of his swift movement knocked Reanna backward. She felt herself start to fall; then, suddenly, she was in his arms. For a moment, neither of them spoke. He stood holding her, his hands around her shoulders. They were so close she could feel the warmth of his body against her softer one—the strength of his arms surrounding her. The electricity of his touch rippled through her.

Confused by the sensations rampaging through her, and not quite knowing what else to do, she gestured at the horse. "He seems to present quite a challenge."

"Yes," Travis murmured huskily, still staring down at her. "Quite a challenge."

Were they discussing Iron Scimitar? Somehow, Reanna didn't think so. She looked up at him, her thick, dark lashes shielding vulnerable brown eyes. He was studying her just as intently as she was studying him. Then, abruptly, he let her go.

She turned away and drew a deep breath. "I was looking for Andy."

"He's inside the barn with my father." His speech was terse. Succinct. Abrupt. What was his problem? Every since they'd spoken in the car, he'd been remote, angry.

"Oh." What else should she say? Should she go now?

But David had brought the colt to the rail. He called to her, "Hi, Reanna, how's your father?"

Glad to turn from Travis and the turmoil she felt whenever she was near him, she wheeled around to where David was reining in Scimitar. She shielded her eyes from the sun as she replied, "He's going to be fine, thanks. Since when are you playing jockey?"

"Since Travis can't get anyone else to ride this beast," David said, laughing. "None of the exercise boys will touch him. They think he's a gray devil."

"Have Charlie cool him out and give him a bath," Travis snapped at his brother. "We'll spend the rest of the day working with a few of the yearlings."

David nodded, seeming not to notice Travis's short, ill-tempered tone. "What was his time?"

"One thirty-eight for the mile."

"Slow." David shook his head. "He had plenty, he just wouldn't give it. I couldn't get anything out of him these past few days, either. Maybe the exercise boys are right. Are you a gray devil?" he asked the horse.

Travis sighed. "With this kind of response, and losing

all those days, he's never going to be ready for the Sanford."

David shrugged his agreement. "I think we should sell
him now, while we can get our money out of him. As far as
I'm concerned, we're wasting our time."

Reanna frowned as she watched the horse paw nervously at the ground, prancing his dainty hooves in a tattoo
against the firm-packed track. Like most race horses, he
was high-strung, but there was something else wrong with
him. She didn't have time to consider what was bothering
Scimitar, however, for just then, Andy came barreling
around the side of the building.

"Mom! Uncle Travis! Come quick. You gotta see the
kittens! They already growed."

Reanna smiled at her son. It always amazed her that
little things, like a kitten growing, could be such a delight
in the eyes of a child. When did the enthusiasm end and the
jaded attitude begin? Was it just adulthood that brought
cynicism?

"Can I have one?" he went on. "Can I have one as a
pet? Gramps said it was okay if you and Uncle Travis—
Dad," he corrected, "said so."

Mr. Martin had joined them, glancing at her apologetic-
ally. Reanna hated to disappoint her son, but there wasn't
much choice. "I don't think so, Andy. Jenny's allergic to
the hair."

Andy's face fell, but he turned to Travis. How quickly
children learned. "Aw, please? Please, Dad? Can't I have
one? Just one of 'em. There won't be much hair."

Thankfully, Travis backed her up. "No, I don't think
that's a good idea, Andy. The kittens have to stay here with
their mommy. They need their mommy. You can understand that, can't you?"

Andy thought for a moment. "Yeah, I guess."

"But you can have another pet," Travis added. "Maybe

we can get you some fish. You wanted an aquarium, didn't you?"

"Nah, I don't want a fish."

"What *would* you like, then?" Travis was puzzled.

"A horse!" Andy said, suddenly full of enthusiasm. "I want a horse of my own."

"Well, a horse isn't exactly a pet," Travis countered hesitantly. "You'd have to leave it at the stables."

"I know that."

"And you'd have to take care of it."

"I know that!" This time Andy was more enthusiastic. "I can do it! I can brush him and feed him and pet him, just like Charlie. And I won't forget. I promise."

Clearly, Travis was in a corner. Reanna was amazed, though, at how well he was handling Andy. He laughed and swung the child on his shoulders. "We'll see," he answered finally. "Don't you have a birthday coming up soon?"

"Aw, that's too far away. I don't wanna wait that long."

"Humm." Travis pretended to frown. "Maybe the birthday fairy will come early."

Andy's frown was real. "You're not a very 'sperienced dad. Don't you know there's no such thing as a birthday fairy? It's the tooth fairy."

This time, Travis roared. "Sure there's a birthday fairy. Just ask Mrs. Mackey, she'll tell you. The birthday fairy comes here all the time."

Watching them interact, Reanna was struck with a sudden sadness. What would happen when she and Travis divorced? Andy would miss him, just as Jenny would miss her. Why were children so often the ones most hurt by adult decisions?

"Speaking of Mrs. Mackey," Mr. Martin said to Andy, "I think we should get back for lunch. Thelma's fixing something special today."

"Oh, boy, hamburgers!" Forgetting his birthday present, the kittens, and everything else, Andy started off toward the house. Reanna was glad to follow.

After lunch, feeling at loose ends, she wandered around the house for most of the day. She didn't know what to do with her time. She'd glanced in on Jenny and Mrs. Webber once, but hadn't interfered. As a teacher herself, she understood how difficult it could be to establish a rapport. Then she'd started to help Thelma, but the housekeeper had shooed her, in no uncertain terms, out of the kitchen. All she was supposed to do was choose menus.

All through dinner, she felt out of place, too. She toyed with her food, only occasionally asking a polite question. Since she had managed to sit across from Travis, she wasn't disturbed by his touches, but she found his glances increasingly distressing. Why was he watching her? He also seemed to be trying to figure out the answer to that question. Many times Reanna looked up to see him watching her, studying her intently. It was obvious he still didn't trust her.

After they ate, Reanna went into the kitchen, insisting that she would help with dishes. But Thelma evicted her again. With nothing to do, she paused by the study door. Travis was sprawled in the middle of the floor, coloring in a book with Andy. She watched them for several minutes. He looked so incongruous and yet so comfortable in the role of a father. He chatted easily with his son, talking about purple horses and pink polka-dotted tigers. She turned and went outside, flopping onto the swing on the closed-in porch. It had become one of her favorite places, almost a hideaway, away from the rest of the family where she could be alone. There was a clear view of the estate, and of the horses grazing. Many nights she had sat listening to the crickets' chirping and the horses' soft shuffling.

It was several hours later that she went in search of

Andy. The study doors were closed, so she assumed her son was somewhere upstairs. Perhaps Thelma was giving him a bath.

Andy was wet, all right, but hardly bathed. Reanna found him in the midst of playing submarine. Water was all over the bathroom, and so were millions of bubbles that he had poured into the sink. "Andy!" she admonished.

"Hi, Mom!" He looked up happily. "Wanna play?"

"Andy, this room is a mess."

He glanced around at the wet towels and puddles of water. "Uh-oh," he said. "Are you gonna be mad?"

Not in the mood to scold him, Reanna laughed and flicked a soap bubble at him. A full-scale water battle ensued, with both of them giggling and soaking wet. After giving him a bath, she cleaned the room, picking up discarded clothes and toys. As she tucked him into bed and read him a story, she couldn't help but notice that the picture of the polka-dotted tiger was pinned to his bulletin board.

"Dad made it," he said, following the direction of her gaze. "I colored a horse."

Reanna nodded. How quickly children adjusted. Now it was Dad and not Uncle Travis. She wished she was as comfortable with the role change. She leaned over for a kiss. "Good night, Andy."

He gave her a sleepy hug. "'Night, Mom. Love you. Say good night to Dad, too."

There were a lot of things she wanted to say to Travis, including thank you. She felt guilty for not saying it already. It was the least she owed him for his support the past few days, and perhaps if she confronted him, she could find out what was bothering him. Intent on her mission, she walked to the stables.

Charlie was sitting in front of Scimitar's stall, whittling.

Reanna heard the horse before she saw him. He was kicking at his stall and generally making a fuss.

"He sounds rambunctious tonight," she said. "Where's his stablemate?"

Nearly all racehorses had a stablemate, another animal who kept them company and served as a calming influence. Other horses, goats, pigs, and even chickens were pressed into service. Often, with all the animals running around in the field, a racetrack looked more like a barnyard.

"Huh! It'd take more'n a stablemate to calm that devil down. He's a mean 'un. Thought it might help if I sat here, but it ain't done nothing. I swear he's the only horse I know who has to have a padded stall so's he won't hurt hisself."

Reanna laughed at the groom's disgust and leaned over the half door. "Hi, boy," she called softly. "What's the matter?"

Scimitar looked at her and snorted. Just then, chased by a sibling, one of the kittens Andy had been playing with earlier that afternoon scampered into the stall from the back entrance.

"Let me get him, quick," Charlie called. "That horse'll trample the poor thing."

Without thinking of danger, Reanna unlatched the door and walked into the stall, but before either she or the groom could react, the kitten stood in front of Scimitar and meowed. It was a lost, lonely sound. Surprisingly, the big horse shook his mane and lowered his head, nickering softly.

"Well, I'll be," Charlie said. "Look at that."

Reanna laughed, watching as Scimitar allowed the kitten to rub against his legs. The kitten meowed again and curled up in the hay. "I guess he has a stablemate after all," she said.

"Guess so," the groom agreed, watching the horse and cat interact. "Maybe it'll help."

For some reason, it was suddenly important for Reanna to win the horse over herself. She reached into her pocket for the small packets of raisins she kept for Jenny and Andy. "Here, boy," she called.

The horse turned to her and pawed the stall floor. Reanna stood her ground with the raisins in her palm. Looking at her with his eyes wild, Scimitar hesitated for the longest time. Finally, he took a step forward.

"Come on," she called, "it won't be so bad. All I'll do is rub your neck."

"Better watch it, miss. He's still a mean 'un." Charlie was clearly nervous. This was his domain, and if anything happened to Reanna, he would catch hell.

"Come on." She clucked again, moving forward and holding out the raisins.

The horse slowly continued his trek. He paused in front of her and snuffled the fruit from her hand. His mouth was soft, and yet at the same time ticklish. Pleased that he had trusted her enough to come to her, she patted his neck and reached to scratch behind his ears.

"Huh!" Charlie was clearly disgusted. "If that ain't just like a male. Wooed by a soft voice and a little bit of sweet. For the past month, I ain't been able to get near this hoss without his biting me."

"I guess we all have our weakness, Charlie."

Reanna swung abruptly around. Travis was standing behind them at the entrance to the stall. How long had he been watching? She couldn't tell if he was angry or not. His expression was closed. From behind, Scimitar nudged her, wanting more fruit. Ignoring the facetious remark, she turned back to the horse and fed him a few more raisins. Then she leaned down and ran a hand over his legs, looking for hot spots. All afternoon she had thought about his behavior.

"There's not a lame bone in his body," Travis said quietly, evidently unperturbed at finding her in the stall with his most expensive racehorse. "I thought that, too, at first, but he's been poked and prodded and examined, and there's not a damned thing wrong with him. I'm beginning to think David's right. Perhaps I should sell him."

Reanna watched Scimitar for a while. Finally, she turned and left the stall. Travis closed the door behind them. "Bed him down, Charlie."

"Yessir, boss." The groom nearly bowed, obviously happy he wasn't being chastised for allowing Reanna inside the stall.

"The maiden race he won," Reanna asked, "was it a sloppy track?"

Travis glanced at her as they fell into step, heading toward the house. "Yes. It had rained for two days straight. The track was pure mud."

"Have you tried padding his feet?"

"No." He paused, looking pensive as he shoved his hands in his pockets. "Do you think he has tender feet?"

Reanna also paused. For the first time since they'd left her father's bedside, she felt herself relax in Travis's presence. "I know it sounds silly, but I remember my father telling me about a Triple Crown winner years ago that had special horseshoes padded with piano felt. If Scimitar acts lame and there's nothing wrong with him, why not try softening the impact on his hooves? It might work."

"I don't know. That's quite a long shot." Travis's expression was still thoughtful. His brow was furrowed, and his eyebrows formed a dark slash across his forehead. Then he shrugged. "What the hell, you might be right. I've tried everything else, except to paint him another color."

Reanna smiled, amazed. "I find it hard to believe you subscribe to that superstition."

"I try to deny it," he said with a wry smile. Another first. It seemed genuine good humor. "But I cross my fingers and my toes and sometimes my eyes if I think it will give me luck. And like any horseman, I do the same thing before each race." He paused. "Perhaps that's my problem with Scimitar. Maybe I should change my tactics."

"What do you do before a race?" Reanna was truly interested. Some of the habits of horsemen were amusing.

"I pace, smoke a cigar, eat oysters."

She laughed, feeling strangely carefree. They were under an old willow tree, and the breeze fluttered through her hair. She leaned against the knobby trunk. "My father used to carry good-luck charms. He said it didn't hurt to have Lady Fortune on your side. And once, when I was wearing an old shirt, we happened to win a race with a horse he had very little confidence in. After that, I had to wear the same shirt each time the horse ran." She looked up at Travis, a smile curving her lips. He, too, was leaning against the tree, his hand close to her cheek. "Even when the blouse got too small, I still had to wear it."

"You were very close to your father, weren't you?"

"Yes, I was, particularly after my mother died."

"I understand you worked together."

"If you want to call it that. I never got my trainer's license, but I used to exercise the horses. When I was little, I always wanted a colt of my own. I was as bad as Andy. I used to plead and beg."

"But you never got one?"

"No. We couldn't afford an expensive Thoroughbred, and then, as I got older, I was content to ride the colts my father worked with. It was like having my own horse. In a way, they were all mine."

"I'm surprised you switched to teaching."

"I like children, too." She laughed again. "It's funny, when I grew out of wanting a horse of my own, all I could think of was being a jockey. I rode in one race. After that, I went to college."

"You lost the race?"

"Miserably. It was in Florida, at the Downs. I was only seventeen, and I thought I could conquer the world. We were left at the starting gate because I was so nervous I forgot to break him. I don't think the horse ever recovered from the shock, either. At least he never won again. Shelly Robbins—you remember her? She never let me forget losing. She teased me unmercifully about it." She paused a few moments, looking at her hands while she tried to find the appropriate words to express her gratitude. Why was it so hard to say thank you? Finally, she just plunged in. "Travis, I don't know how to say this, but I just wanted to thank you for everything you've done for me and my father the past few days."

Guilt tugged at Travis, weighing him down. However inadvertent, he was the cause of her misunderstanding with her father. By his carelessness one night long ago, he'd gotten her pregnant, and she had paid for it.

"You don't have to thank me, Reanna," he said gruffly, remorse roiling inside him, tearing him apart. He wanted to brush back her hair. He wanted to kiss her.

"Yes, I do. And I have to thank you for inviting him here to stay, too." She placed a hand on his arm and glanced at him earnestly, embarrassed by her financial situation. Medical care was expensive, and her father was going to require a great deal of supervision. She wanted Travis to know how grateful she was; his offer would make the burden easier. "I don't know what my father's insurance situation is, but there are going to be a lot of bills . . ."

Suspicion, fed by deep-seated mistrust and long-standing doubts, abruptly replaced any tenderness he was feeling. Or perhaps it was that guilt nagging at him. Whatever it was, Travis was suddenly wary. What was she getting at? "The hospital bill has already been paid, Reanna."

"Oh." The surprise in her tone came out as a husky whisper. She hadn't known that. How would she repay him? "All I have is a small savings account, and there are so many things he's going to need. You've been so kind, I hate to ask, but I—I'm going to need some—"

"I noticed you kept the pearls."

She didn't bother to deny his statement. "What does that have to do with this?" she asked, confused.

"How much do you want?" It was an angry accusation.

"How much what do I want?"

"Is this a new ploy, Reanna? This earnest appeal? Do you really think if you pretend gratitude I'll give you money? I paid your father's bills, what more do you want? A little cash on the side?"

"Just what are you intimating?" she asked sharply, almost dreading the answer. So that was how it would be now. Cutting animosity, distrust, and misunderstandings would stand between them, clouding the situation.

"You know very well what I'm intimating. I am surprised, though, at your boldness. As much as I distrusted you these past weeks, I never thought you would stoop low enough to use your father for mercenary gain."

"Is that what you think?" She felt as though he'd slapped her in the face. And here she'd been trying to thank him! To ask for time to repay him! Why did he always assume the worst where she was concerned? "Is that what you believe?"

"Can you deny it? Can you stand here and deny that you weren't using your father's illness to get money from me?" His lips twisted into a contemptuous smile. "Did you think that after our . . . *closeness* at the hospital you could fool me?"

"I don't have to deny a thing, Travis," she said softly, "and I don't have to justify my behavior. But just for the record, I wasn't asking for money. I doubt if you'll believe that, and frankly, I don't care anymore. I'm tired of defending myself, and I'm tired of trying to convince you of my innocence. I'll make it perfectly clear once and for all. As far as I'm concerned, you and your money can go straight to hell."

With that, she turned on her heel and stalked away.

CHAPTER EIGHT

RESENTMENT SEETHED INSIDE Reanna as she sat in a chair in the bedroom, putting curlers in her hair. She'd been trying to show Travis her gratitude, and he'd repaid her with insults. She stuck a bobby pin savagely through the roller. As usual, he'd purposely misconstrued her motives. But he'd clearly been astonished at her outburst. Remembering the look on his face as she'd dressed him down and stormed off brought a smile to her lips. Good. In the future he was going to be more astonished.

Reanna poked another pin into her hair. Tomorrow her head was going to ache from all this torture. Was vengeance worth the suffering she would endure? Yes, she assured herself. At least she wouldn't have to worry about her neck aching, as it had that first night they'd spent together. She knew exactly where she was going to sleep. They had shared a bed the past few days—they could certainly share one now. She had every intention of making herself comfortable in his bedroom. As he'd pointed out, this was her room now, and she'd purposely made her mark on it. Her clothing was strewn across chairs, her makeup was interspersed among Travis's things on the oak dresser, and she'd littered the bathroom with her toiletries. Because she was piqued, she placed the filmy white negligee she'd worn the last few nights in the bottom of the bureau drawer, once again pulling out an ugly flannel gown.

Then she clasped the pearls around her throat. She'd found them in, of all places, her purse. Thelma must have put them there while packing her case, or perhaps she'd put them there herself. She couldn't remember now, but it didn't matter. All she wanted to do was taunt Travis by wearing them.

For a moment, as she stared at her reflection, an alarming thought occurred to her. If she didn't know better, she'd swear she was attracted to Travis Martin. Otherwise, why was she going to all this trouble just to get his attention? She *was* trying to get his attention, there was no denying that. But why? Why would she behave so uncharacteristically? There were occasions, she had to admit, when he could be charming, kind, and thoughtful. And he was a handsome man—tall, well built, with a ruggedness born of hard labor. Yet despite that rugged demeanor, there was an aura about him that spoke of a person accustomed to luxury and gentility. No wonder. The Martins were a family steeped in southern tradition.

Still deep in thought, she started to cream her face. Travis was different from the other Martins, however. He must be a throwback, she decided, to some ancient rakehell ancestor—a pirate perhaps, or maybe a handsome cutthroat. That would account for his attitude being so unlike that of his father and brothers. Most of the time he was maddening and arrogant and rude and overbearing and she couldn't think of what-all else. The list of his faults was endless.

Surprised, and feeling just a bit guilty at her peevish contemplations, she swung around when the bedroom door opened. Travis took in everything in a single glance: the nightgown, the curlers, the cream she was spreading on her face. A single dark eyebrow lifted perceptively.

"I see you've brought out your Christian Dior."

Running a hand over the gown, she pretended ignorance of his actual intent. "Lovely, isn't it?"

"Quite." He stepped inside the room and closed the

door. "Too bad it's wasted. Or have you forgotten that we didn't marry because of any burning desire?"

Reanna smiled sweetly, and with as much aplomb as she could manage under the circumstances, swept across the room to the bed. She flipped back the covers. "Which one of us are you trying to convince, Travis? I haven't forgotten. All I'm interested in is money and when I can get it."

"No doubt." Casually, watching her, he started to strip off his shirt with a taunting smirk. "I take it you plan to sleep in my bed?"

"Our bed," she corrected. "Yes, I do plan to sleep in it. It's big enough for two. That is, if you don't hog the covers."

"I'll try to share." The lazy note in his deep voice was laced with sarcasm. Now he was taking off his boots. They clattered to the floor as he continued, "By the way, I haven't had time to see a lawyer about Andy's adoption yet. I'm afraid we'll have to prolong our irreconcilable differences for a few more weeks."

"That's fine. Take your time." She fingered the pearls around her neck with one hand, and with the other gestured to indicate the opulence of the room. "I'm rather enjoying all this, being mistress of the house and everything. I do need some new clothes, though, to go with my exalted position. I think I'll go shopping tomorrow," she continued thoughtfully. "I haven't lived in Lexington very long. Are there any designer shops nearby?"

"I thought you only had a small bank account."

"Oh"—she forced a gay laugh—"I won't *buy* them. I'll charge them. All I have to do is mention your name. Do you happen to know of any good jewelry stores? I need some earrings to go with the pearls."

"Really? And what if I don't pay for all these new baubles?"

"You're forgetting how devious I am, Travis. In this

state, a husband is responsible for his wife's debts. Surely you knew that . . ." She smiled ever so sweetly and went on, pretending to be appalled. "Don't tell me . . . you didn't know that minor legal fact? Now that I think about it, charge accounts weren't covered in the premarital agreement. Too bad."

"Your attitude changes from one moment to the next, Reanna. Earlier, you were extolling your innocence. I believe your exact words were that both I and my money could go to hell."

"Haven't you discovered by now that I'm fickle? That's a prerogative we women like to exercise. I've decided not to bother to try to fool you. Oh," she went on in the same saccharine tone, "several invitations to dinner came in the mail. Shall I accept?"

"Please do, if you think you can get through them." He paused, turning to her. "Just remember, we'll have to pretend to be lovers."

Reanna shrugged with what she hoped was an air of casual indifference. "I think I can manage."

"I'm sure you will." Then he was taking off his pants, blithely, as though she weren't in the room. She watched, strangely mesmerized by the sight of his body. His legs were long and lean, like the rest of him. Hard, sinewy thighs were covered with dense, dark hair; his muscles flexed as he lifted one leg, and then the other.

Suddenly, she looked up, her eyes drawn to his. He was watching her, too, assessing her reaction. Their wills clashed in yet another silent battle; he daring her to continue her perusal, she daring him to continue undressing. Although she felt mortified, Reanna refused to turn away. It was a matter of principle. If she were to waver, it would seem cowardly.

Moments later, as he removed his brief underwear, she wished she had chosen the timorous approach. She fixed her gaze on the gray of his eyes, trying not to see what her vision encompassed. It was only a matter of seconds, but for what seemed an eternity he stood there in front of her, his eyes challenging her. Then, without a word, he strolled, naked, to the bathroom.

Reanna lay in the bed, her face burning with anger. Damn the man! If it took every ounce of self-control she possessed, she would not allow him to perturb her. And if it took the rest of her life, she would pay him back the money he'd spent on her father's hospital bills.

By the time he came out of the shower, a towel draped around his lower body, she had controlled her rampaging emotions. She feigned interest in a magazine as he strolled around the room, preparing for bed. Yet she was aware of every move, every footfall. Finally, the bed creaked with his weight. She snapped off the light.

"Good night, Travis," she said pleasantly.

"Good night, Reanna."

In the darkness of the room, Travis tried to examine the events of the day. It was something he'd done for ages, and quite often, if he pondered long enough, he discovered the solution to a troubling dilemma. But his problems were normally limited to horses. Tall, beautiful, stubborn women were usually the least of his worries. Reanna Williamson Martin posed a puzzle in which there seemed to be no ready answers. She hadn't given him a single reason to trust her; she'd given him every reason to mistrust her. Then why the hell did he want to believe in her?

Sighing in frustration, Travis grabbed his robe, slammed the door, and went downstairs.

It was unspoken, but the truce was declared. For the next two weeks Reanna and Travis behaved like civilized enemies, polite but with undercurrents of hostility. If at all possible, they avoided each other. They went to dinners and parties, all the while pretending they were lovers. There were moments when Reanna almost believed it herself, and then they went home and the cold war continued.

Sultry heat and humidity had ushered in August. With little else to do, Reanna divided her time between visiting her father at the hospital and getting Andy ready for kindergarten. The list of clothes her son needed seemed endless: new jeans, gym shoes, jackets, shirts, and sweaters. As she withdrew more and more funds from her rapidly diminishing bank account, she felt desperate. What would she do if Andy got sick? How would she pay for the doctor? But since her son wasn't sick, she refused to ask Travis for money.

Instead, she pretended that she had charged item after item to his bank. She did buy a few dresses, but not with his money and not at a designer shop. She would slip something old, or something she found on a reduced rack, into some boxes Thelma had saved from several exclusive downtown stores and leave them lying around where he would find them. When he would ask her about the cost, she would shrug and act as though she hadn't the vaguest idea of when he would be billed. At every opportunity, she wore the pearls.

Combined with the seasonal heat, the tension became unbearable. Determined not to give up her comfort, Reanna slept in the king-sized bed, and just as stubbornly, she wore the flannel gowns and wrapped her hair in curlers. If it disturbed Travis, she didn't know, for he came in the room late at night, after she'd fallen asleep. Before she woke up, he was gone.

Travis spent the day at the stables, working with Iron Scimitar. Now that his hooves were padded, the horse was much more content to run. Still, he had a nasty disposition, and his bad habits were even harder to break, but on the track he was well behaved, no longer lugging in at the rail.

Every evening, Reanna slipped to the stables to see him. He would nudge her, expecting raisins each time.

No one was more surprised than Reanna the day Travis asked her to accompany them to the Sanford. She stood for several moments just staring at him. "What?" she finally got out.

"I thought you might want to go to Saratoga Springs with us," he repeated. Andy and the horse were the only two subjects they could discuss without arguing. "You suggested the pads for Scimitar's feet. I thought you might want to watch his first race."

"I'd love to go," she said, quickly accepting the invitation. It had been years since she had been to a racetrack. She was excited just thinking about it. "What about Andy, though?"

"We'll only be gone a couple days. I want to ship Scimitar in by plane at the last moment. I think he gets nervous at the track, and the kitten is still too young to take long trips."

Scimitar had become very attached to the kitten these past weeks. As much as he kicked and pawed, the big horse never came near enough to hurt the cat. It would rub and purr at his legs, and at night they slept together on the stacks of fresh hay.

"David's coming, too. It will be just the three of us, and of course, Charlie."

"What about the plane ride? Do you think Scimitar will have any ill effects?"

Travis shook his head. "Considering all his other bad habits, that horse travels well. It will only take us a few hours versus two days in a van."

Reanna spent the next day getting ready. On Friday, the day before the race, she said good-bye to Andy and went with Travis and David to the airport. Scimitar kicked and bucked going into the plane, and she had a moment's worry that he would make the flight miserable. Charlie winked at her as he fed the horse a handful of raisins. In less than three hours, they were landing in New York.

While Travis settled the horse into a barn, Reanna looked around the racetrack, half expecting to see her father. If he continued his progress, he'd be discharged from the hospital soon. She could see him now, marching around the track trading insults with his cronies and discussing the merits of one horse versus another.

Nestled in the middle of the Catskills, Saratoga Race Track sat like a dowager off Union Avenue in the midst of tree-laden countryside, famous for its healing waters. Here, among the gentry of the racing world, the usually frenetic life of horsemen slowed to a lazy, hazy pace. Cupolas dominated the roofline of the grandstand, and cascades of petunias and geraniums spilled from the second-floor balconies. Red-and-white candy-cane stripes decorated the stands. The contagious exhilaration of Thoroughbred racing was like a fire in her blood. Reanna skipped around, just enjoying the sights.

They spent that night in a nearby hotel. Naturally, she had brought her nighttime paraphernalia, but she didn't need it. Travis was preoccupied, and Reanna was so nervous she hardly noticed his presence in the room. They were up at dawn, dressing. This was the day of reckoning for the gray colt, and Reanna hadn't realized until this moment how desperately she wanted Scimitar to win.

She thought the race would never begin. She stood along the rail, close to where David and Travis were saddling the horse under the graceful elms, and waited, her stomach tied in knots. They had spent the day grooming and exercising Scimitar and just wandering around the track. Now, it was time. It was the moment of truth. There were eight other Thoroughbreds entered in the race, all of them among the best two-year-olds in the nation.

When the starting bell rang and the horses shot off, Reanna was unprepared for the jolt of excitement that nestled in her throat. Her heart pounded with each step the animals made. Scimitar was running well, settling in behind the front leader, Lynda's Pride, a bay filly with marvelous configuration. Unfortunately, "settled in" were the words of the day. The big colt never moved from the filly's flank. As they crossed the finish line, Scimitar was second, and Reanna knew he'd hardly reached stride. What in the world had happened? Travis must be wondering, too, Reanna thought, only he wasn't as outwardly calm as she was. In fact, Reanna had never seen him so irritated.

"A filly," he muttered in disgust. "He was beaten by a filly."

They left for Kentucky that night. On the flight home, David and Travis argued while Scimitar stomped and snorted in the back of the plane. Now Travis was convinced the horse was a loser, and David was the believer.

"He was following that filly," the younger brother kept insisting. "I tell you, she was in heat."

"I'm selling him" was all Travis said.

"Give him another chance," David argued. "He's already entered in the Hopeful. Race him one more time. Now that his feet don't hurt, he's well behaved."

"Sure, now that his feet don't hurt, he strolls around the track sniffing fillies!"

"Put Marcos up on him."

"Another jockey isn't going to make a difference. The horse is a loser, period."

David sighed and glanced at the big colt. "What do you think, Reanna?"

She didn't have an answer. "Lynda's Pride was awfully pretty. At least Scimitar recognizes quality."

She wanted to make a comment about females being the

downfall of the male species, but refrained. Travis was already furious.

When they returned to Martin Oaks, the entire family already knew about the defeat. Travis and Mr. Martin conferred for hours. Reanna went upstairs to put Andy to bed, then on to her room. She felt tired. The events of the day had certainly been fatiguing. She was almost ready for bed when Travis came into the room. He seemed more irritated than ever. He took one look at her and slammed the door.

"Your face is starting to look like an oil well, Reanna."

She was surprised that he was directing his anger at her. She turned back to the mirror, but Travis was evidently spoiling for an argument.

"And your hair is getting frizzy from those ridiculous rollers," he went on.

It was the insult in his tone that made her answer. "What do you care? I don't see that my face and hair are any of your concern."

"I have to sleep with you."

"Then don't," she snapped back, glaring at him. "You can always use the chair."

Ignoring her answer, he gestured at her gown. "And if you're going to insist on wearing such ugly nightgowns, the least you could do is buy some different ones so I don't have to look at the same damned yellow vines night after night."

"They're flowers," she retorted, "*green* flowers." Their angry exchange was absurd. What difference did it make if the pattern of her gown was green flowers or yellow vines? Yet she couldn't keep herself from responding. "And I have two gowns. They're both alike. If you don't like them, don't look at them."

"That's a bit difficult, considering you parade in front of me night after night."

"Parade in front of you!" she repeated, her temper soaring at his retort. "Parade in front of you! *You're* the one who parades in front of *me*, walking around in your towel and stripping off your clothes as though I'm not even in the room!" That he'd only undressed in front of her that one night didn't register in her agitated state. Unthinking, she blurted out the truth. "And for your information, because of my new, elevated status in this household, I don't have the money to buy new nightgowns. Since I don't teach Jenny anymore, I don't get paid, and I've spent what little I had on new school clothes for Andy."

"Then charge it," he snarled back. "You charge everything else. There are boxes all over this house. And surely you have something besides that hideous thing! Even a feed sack would be preferable."

"Yes!" she said, hotly. "Yes, I do have something else." Spurred by anger beyond her control, Reanna slammed the brush down and stripped off her nightgown. In a rage, she found the filmy negligee Thelma had given her and pulled it on. Then, ripping out the curlers, she faced him. "There, how's this? No flowers, no vines! No green or yellow!"

Travis stood staring at her, his mouth half-open with astonishment. Then, just as quickly, his shock was gone, replaced by a searing look of undisguised passion. Slowly, so slowly it was almost a caress, he let his gaze trail over her body—down along the soft curve of her breasts, and farther, to the dark triangle between her thighs. The gown was so sheer that her legs and the dusky tips of her breasts were clearly visible. Her hair had fallen down, cascading around her shoulders, and her chest heaved from her rapid gasps.

The desire flickering and smoldering in his eyes alarmed Reanna, and at the same time, excited her. As she met his gaze, defiance and anger fled like dry leaves in the wake of a storm. Her breath caught in her throat. For once, their needs were attuned. The same rampaging emotions shivered through her, and she waited, half expecting him to take her into his arms and kiss her.

But he turned abruptly away and tossed several bills onto the dresser. "Andy is my responsibility. Whenever you need anything for him, you are to tell me."

Without a further word or a glance in her direction, he slammed from the room. Reanna glared at the money, then ripped it from the dresser and put it with the pearls. She hadn't charged a dime to him, but she'd be damned if she would admit it.

She tossed restlessly most of the night. For some inexplicable reason, she missed Travis. All these nights she'd lain in bed beside him, and there were many times, she knew, that she had curled up in his arms. Waking, she had quickly turned over, and as long as he hadn't mentioned it, neither had she. It was late before she finally heard him come back into the room. He paused a few moments, looking at her, then flopped onto one of the chairs.

Pretending she was asleep, Reanna listened until his breathing was deep and even. The next thing she knew, gray light was streaming in through the window, throwing the room into shadowed relief.

Travis was still asleep in the chair, his lanky body cramped, one hand thrown over the side, and his long legs stretched out across the carpet. He was still fully dressed, including his boots. An air of vulnerability softened the normally harsh lines of his face, and he looked drawn and tired. A single lock of hair fell down over his forehead, and a dark stubble of beard shadowed his thrusting jawline. Even sleeping, his rugged masculinity was readily apparent. Now Reanna could see why at that party five years ago she had been smitten by him. What would it be like, she wondered, to be in love with him . . . to be loved by him?

She lay quietly, watching the even rhythm of his breathing, his chest rising and falling. He was an enigma, this stranger who was her husband. Travis Martin was every woman's dream: strong, dependable, appealing. Yes, he was steely hard, determined in his beliefs, and sometimes exceptionally derisive, but despite his faults he could be kind and thoughtful. In all fairness she had to admit that she had deliberately provoked much of his sarcasm. There were many times, she knew, when she pushed him beyond the limits of endurance, and still, he held his temper. She also had to admit that he was very, very attractive.

And, she finally acknowledged, she was very, very attracted to him. No, that wasn't quite accurate; she was in love with him. The realization was startling, and she stared across the room at him, astounded. She was in love with Travis Martin, and she had been for a long, long time.

But what could she do about it? How did he feel about her? The question loomed in her mind, unanswerable. He was drawn to her sexually. Of that she was nearly certain. The look in his eyes last night had been explosive passion. Could she capitalize on that desire? Could she seduce her husband? Could she make him fall in love with her? She wasn't a very good actress.

Then again, she wouldn't be acting.

She waited until he began to stir before she slipped out of bed and stretched lazily. From the corner of her eye, she could see him watching her; she could feel the intensity of his gaze burning through her as she sauntered off to the bathroom. Moments later, she heard the door slam. The sound reverberated through the room. This time, Reanna was the one who arched a single eyebrow. With a smug smile curving her lips, she took a long, hot shower.

Later that day she went downtown and sought out a fancy lingerie shop.

CHAPTER NINE

NOW THE TABLES were turned. Reanna waited up for Travis each night, parading in front of him in various sheer gowns. She brushed her hair until it shone. Taunting him, she would find excuse after excuse to walk in front of him, to stretch, to bend, to twist her body enticingly. When he snapped at her, she bit her tongue to keep from retorting, smiling pleasantly and looking up at him seductively. When they were in front of people, she touched him constantly, running her hands up his arms, leaning over to kiss him.

At first, Travis seemed puzzled by her extreme reversal. Then, as the days wore on, his bewilderment turned to throbbing sensuality. Each glance was fraught with hunger, with barely checked passion. It wasn't very long before her efforts began to take their toll. If it was possible, he was more surly than ever. Even his father and brothers started to avoid him. Once, Mr. Martin glanced at her for an explanation, but Reanna merely shrugged and walked away. She knew exactly what was bothering her husband, and it delighted her.

She began to spend more and more time at the stables, when he was there, and at night, she no longer turned over when she woke in his arms. Instead, she would sigh and snuggle against him, thrusting her breasts along his bare skin. On those occasions, he would spring quickly from the bed and flop in the chair. He began to shower so much and

139

at such odd times that she was tempted to tease him, but she just watched him and waited.

Reanna knew she was playing with fire, and several nights later, the flames raged out of control. She was wearing a sheer yellow gown with a plunging, lacy bodice that exposed most of her breasts. Travis came into the room just as she had finished brushing her hair and tying a matching ribbon in it.

She turned and smiled at him. "Did you finish your paperwork?"

"Yes." He was leaning against the door looking at her, his stance aggressive, all authoritative male. The searing glance made every cell in her body come tinglingly alive.

"You look tired." She rose to walk toward him, pretending there was something in the closet she wanted to get. "You should get more rest."

"Yes, I suppose I should."

His voice was so low and husky she could barely hear it, and his narrowed eyes were moving slowly over her, taking in the exposed curve of her breast. She walked closer, pausing just in front of him.

"What did you say?"

"Yes, I suppose I should." Louder now, but still husky. "You're up late."

Shrugging, she continued toward the closet. "I had some things to do."

"I see."

Was his answer a purposeful double entendre? What exactly did he see? She reached toward the closet shelf, knowing he was watching, knowing the motion would thrust her breasts forward. For a moment, she felt a definite unease. This was the first time she'd gone this far. Swallowing a tiny lump of apprehension, she turned to him and smiled. "Travis, could you help? I can't seem to reach this box."

Reanna smiled shyly as he stared at her, the stirring inquisition of his gaze compounding her excitement. Slowly, he walked toward her, never taking his eyes from her face. As he reached toward the shelf, they were body to body, the erect tips of her breasts brushing against him, but neither of them moved. What she read in his expression left her breathless, and her pulse quickened in pleasure.

"Thank you," she murmured as he handed her the carton. She started to turn away, but he grasped her arm and jerked her back. The hard wall of his chest crushed her breasts, and his thighs pressed hard against her softness.

"All right, Reanna," he said huskily, "you win. What's your price?"

Suddenly, she was frightened. The harshness of his grip, the intensity of his tone, the firm male flesh pressed close to her body, all combined to make her heart thud with alarm. This time she'd gone too far. "What are you talking about?"

"Let's stop this pretense. You know damned well what I'm talking about. You've been teasing me for days, and you've accomplished your purpose. We both know I want you. What will it take to get you in my bed?"

Despite her anxiety, a triumphant smile curved her lips. "Why, Travis, I thought we didn't marry because of any burning desire. Didn't you tell me once not to bother to try to seduce you? That it wouldn't work?"

"I also told you not to play coy with me. No games, Reanna. I'm calling your bluff."

"I'm not bluffing." She tossed her head back haughtily. "I'm already in your bed. I sleep there every night."

"But I don't," he said. Then he kissed her, harshly, commandingly, his fingers entwined in her hair, holding her so tightly that she could hardly move. She struggled, but his pursuit was relentless as his lips laved hers, the kiss deepening and demanding. There seemed to be no stopping him. The more she fought, the harsher his kiss became. Reanna was panting from a combination of fear and passion. She wanted him. Oh, Lord, she wanted him, but not this way.

Clasping her closer, he pulled her roughly against his hard length. Reanna lost the battle. Succumbing to the more powerful emotion that throbbed and pounded through her veins, she moaned and arched against him as his lips moved ruthlessly over hers. Now his hands were everywhere at once, stroking her breasts, kneading her buttocks, caressing her bare skin. From deep inside her soul, she felt tremors of need shake her body. It was as though she had been swept up in a storm, a maelstrom of rapture. A sweet ache began in her thighs, consuming her, trembling up her body to nestle in the core of her being. She opened her mouth to the sensual invasion of his tongue, her legs to his probing fingers. He trailed tiny kisses along her jaw, down her neck, and along her breasts. Pushing aside the gown, he cupped her breasts, thrusting them forward. His mouth tingled and burned on her flesh as his lips tantalized her nipples. Strangely exhilarated, she gasped again, slumping limply in his arms.

"Oh, God, Reanna," he murmured against her throat. "I want you. I want you so desperately."

It was the tug of his hands on her negligee, ripping it from her body, that brought her back to reality. The rending of the thin fabric sounded like a cannon shot echoing in the room. She started to struggle harder. "No!" she cried, pulling from his arms. "Stop!"

Panting hard, she backed away, her hands crossed over her breasts, holding her gown together. Travis stood with his arms at his sides. The tautness of his control was evident in his stance, in his passion-laden eyes. He still wanted her, that was obvious, but more important, he knew she wanted him.

"What is it, Reanna?" His voice vibrated with a combination of desire and fury. "Holding out for higher stakes? Aren't the dresses and jewels enough?" He walked toward her, his eyes hard, his voice deceptively low. "I don't intend to keep sleeping on the sofa or in the chair. What will it take, Reanna? Name your price. I'm willing to pay."

She'd brought this on herself with her pretense all these weeks, but his assumption still hurt. And what she wanted wasn't money or jewels, but the highest premium of all: his love. She held herself stiffly erect. "I don't have a price, Travis, but if I did, you couldn't afford it."

"Everyone has a price, love," he retorted softly, "both of us included. In the end, we all have a premium to pay. Mine is having to admit that I want you."

Although with that he left the room and didn't return all night, Reanna tossed restlessly in the big bed, trying to sort out her feelings, wondering what to do. She loved him. Why couldn't she tell him that? And why hadn't she let him make love to her? Finally, near dawn, feeling as if she'd accomplished nothing but create more confusion in her mind, she fell asleep.

It was late when she woke up. The family was already at the breakfast table, but her husband's chair was empty.

"Good morning," she greeted the others cheerily. "Is Travis with Scimitar?"

Mr. Martin looked puzzled. "Didn't you know? Travis left this morning for Saratoga Springs. We have two colts entered in the Travers Stakes."

"Oh," she said.

"He was going to swing down into Maryland to buy some breeding stock, too. I'm surprised he didn't tell you."

"I must have forgotten."

"Perhaps it's all the trips he's making this month. I don't understand why he didn't combine them, with Scimitar due at Saratoga for the Hopeful next week."

Reanna suspected she had something to do with the wasted trips, but she didn't say anything. "Who's training Scimitar this week?"

"David stayed home." Mr. Martin sighed. "I'm afraid if he doesn't win this time, Travis is going to sell the colt. That's another thing I don't understand. It's not like Travis to be so impatient, yet that horse has become his Achilles heel."

He looked like he wanted to say something more, but Reanna quickly excused herself before the conversation could become more personal. She didn't want to discuss the fact that she was also her husband's irritant.

The next few days she felt terribly despondent. Irrationally, she had began to view her relationship to Travis as linked with Scimitar's success or failure. She visited the horse every day, making a habit of talking to him, telling him how important it was to win.

By the morning Travis was to return, Reanna was a nervous wreck. What would she say to him? She was keeping busy going through some old magazines when a large box was delivered to the house in her name. Inside were several nightgowns, all flannel and all patterned with yellow vines and green flowers—except for one. It had huge red strawberries embroidered on the bodice. There was no card or message, but she knew who had sent them. Had the situation between them been different, the gesture would have been amusing. As it was, she sat staring at the gowns for ages, puzzling over the meaning of her husband's strange gift.

She was more confused when she went to the stables. She recognized Travis immediately, but she was surprised at the activity going on. The entire household was standing near a corral watching Andy ride around the ring on a small chestnut pony. Jenny was there, too, admiring a new saddle.

"Aunt Reanna," she called, "look at my new saddle."

Reanna ran her fingers over the hand-tooled leather. "Oh, it's lovely, and just your size."

"Hey, Mom! Look at me!"

She turned to her son, her expression mirroring his delight. He was bouncing up and down, not quite accustomed to the rocking motion required to ride a horse. "Be careful," Reanna admonished, laughing. "Hold on tight."

"The birthday fairy came," he shouted back. The words were shuffled between bumps. "It really came and brought Rover."

Reanna smiled and watched Andy, but her entire being was focused on Travis. She could hear him coming up to stand beside her; she could feel the magnetism of his presence.

"Good morning," he said pleasantly.

The easy joviality of his attitude was even more surprising. "Good morning," she replied. "I watched the race on television. It was an exciting finish."

"Majesty's Prince is a fine colt."

"Are you going to syndicate him for stud now?"

"Perhaps, if he wins the Eclipse award."

Travis seemed to be waiting, almost uninterested in his win or the business of breeding horses. Reanna didn't know what else to say. "Thank you for the nightgowns," she finally murmured.

"You're welcome." Smiling at her, he leaned against the rail, his arms crossed over his chest. "I hope you don't mind, but I drew the line at cold cream."

"I've sworn off cold cream." She laughed anxiously. "You were right—my face *was* beginning to look like an oil well."

She shifted uncomfortably, not knowing how to broach the subject she wanted to discuss.

Travis nodded at Andy. "How do you like the pony?"

"Rover?"

"Not just Rover, but *Red* Rover."

"That sounds like Andy," she said, smiling again.

"Yes," Travis agreed, "it does. He was determined to come up with an authentic name. At first he was disappointed that the pony wasn't purple. He wanted to call it People Eater."

She laughed. "I guess we're lucky he didn't expect pink polka dots."

"Speaking of polka dots, I have a surprise for you, too."

Reanna was stunned as Travis led a dappled gray mare from the stables and brought her over. She was saddled and bridled, ready to ride.

"Well, what do you think?" he asked.

"She's beautiful," Reanna said, admiring the horse.

At about sixteen hands, the mare was trim and yet deep-chested. Her haunches were firm, and her legs straight and narrow. A white blaze ran from her forehead to her nose.

Unable to resist, Reanna ran a hand over the velvet muzzle. "Breeding stock?"

"Strictly pleasure," Travis answered. "She's a hunter. Eventually, I'd like to breed her to Excalibur. Would you like to ride her?"

Speechless, Reanna stared at him. "Me?" she finally got out. "Could I?"

"Come on, I'll give you a boost up. She's still a bit skittish, so be careful."

Suspicion was the furthest thing from Reanna's mind, until she was on the horse and staring down at Travis. Suddenly, she realized why he was in such a good mood, and why he was allowing her to ride the mare. He was buying her. Just the thought made her angry. She slid from the saddle and flicked the reins back to him.

"Your bid is too low, Travis." Before he could answer, she turned on her heel and stalked past a surprised Mr.

Martin, Andy, Jenny, and Thelma, who was cleaning a mirror in the foyer, and clattered up the steps to their room.

She slammed the door closed, but Travis burst into the room behind her, slamming it again. A muscle in his cheek twitched ominously. "All right, Reanna. Just what the hell was that supposed to mean?"

She whirled around. "I think I made myself perfectly clear. Your bid is too low."

"Last week you told me you couldn't be bought, Reanna. I was beginning to believe you. Which is it? Are you for sale or not?"

"My price for a night of passion is a little higher than a ride on a horse or a few nightgowns," she shot back.

"I wasn't offering you a ride," he said softly. His eyes had hardened to that steely gray. "I was giving you the mare. And it didn't have a damn thing to do with bribing you. You told me you had always wanted a horse, and like an idiot, I bought you one. It was a gift, because fool that I am I thought we could make something out of this farce."

Surprised, she could only stare at him. She felt like the idiot and fool he had professed to be. "Travis, I—"

"These are Andy's adoption papers," he interrupted tersely, tossing a thick envelope on the bed between them. "Sign them so one of us can file for divorce."

"Travis . . ." she started again, but he stalked to the door.

"The sooner the better."

Reanna opened the envelope with trembling fingers and stared at the papers through tear-blurred eyes. Was this the way it would end between them? She tried several times to read the legal terminology, but was unable to decipher the contents. The only thing that leaped out at her was the date of his signature. It was the day after their wedding.

Late that night, Reanna sat on the screened-in porch, still thinking about the adoption papers. She twisted her wedding ring around and around on her finger, as though the motion would give her the answers to her questions. These past weeks, Travis had sat on the papers, and once he had even told her he hadn't had time to see a lawyer. And that afternoon, he'd given her a horse. Or at least he had *tried* to give her the horse. She was as bad as he was, jumping to conclusions, making accusations. What did it all mean? Did he care for her after all?

Unseeing, she stared at the pearls and the money on her lap. If only she could convince him of her sincerity. If only she could undo all the mistakes. She was sitting in the swing, trying to decide how to approach him, when he came onto the porch. At dinner he'd been absent, the door to his study closed. Not wanting to face his rejection, she'd been too frightened to knock.

She watched him walk to the windows and look out, unaware of her presence. "Travis," she called softly.

He swung around, surprised. An expression of pleasure, quickly masked, crossed his features. "Reanna. I didn't realize you were here."

"It's one of my favorite places," she said.

"Mine, too." He turned back to the windows. The silence stretched interminably.

"Travis, I've signed the adoption papers."

She saw him nod. "Do you want to file for divorce, or shall I?"

For a moment, icy fear clutched at her stomach. She would have to swallow more than her pride. What she was about to do was risky, and if she was wrong, she would have to suffer the consequences. "I don't want to file for divorce," she said. "I—I was wrong, Travis. I do have a price." She licked her lips nervously and gave a short half laugh. "In fact, it's a very cheap price."

He had turned around. She was looking at her hands, but she was aware of his gaze burning through her. For some reason, it gave her hope, as well as the courage to continue.

"All I want is some more time. I wondered if you'd consent to staying married for another month." Her throat was so dry with the fear of losing him that she could hardly talk. She took a deep breath. "And I don't expect you to sleep on the sofa anymore, or the chair in our room. I—I want you to sleep in our bed"—the rest came out as a mere whisper—"with me."

There was another long silence. She could hear the crickets chirping and the breeze rustling the leaves of a tree. The moon bathed the lawn with pale light. Somewhere in the house, a door slammed. She closed her eyes and took another trembling breath.

"Reanna, I can't—"

"Please let me finish," she said, rising from the swing and walking toward him. "Or I'll never tell you how I really feel." She held out the pearls his father had given her, along with the money he had tossed on her dresser several weeks ago. "I never charged those clothes, and I didn't buy any jewels. I was pretending. I don't want anything from you but a chance to prove to you that I'm not after your money." Before she could lose her courage, she removed her wedding band and placed it in his hand. "I don't want to give this up, but you gave it to me for the wrong reasons. It should be offered in mutual love and trust and belief."

"I thought you didn't want a divorce."

His tone was brusque and harsh, but this time it didn't frighten or anger her. She suddenly understood that it was a defense against pain, against hurt. He was vulnerable, too. Why hadn't she realized that before? She clutched her hands together determinedly.

"I don't want a divorce. I'm returning your ring as proof of my sincerity. I want to make something of our marriage,

Travis, but that's not possible as long as material things stand between us. I'm giving back your ring because... because I love you, and I can only hope that you care for me."

"Reanna, do you realize what you're saying?"

"Yes." She looked up at him, meeting his gaze. "Yes, I realize what I'm saying. All I'm asking for is a month."

"What if it doesn't work after a month? What if we don't love each other?"

"I'm willing to take that chance. As I said, my price is cheap. I want us to be husband and wife in every sense of the word, even if it doesn't work out." She paused, but only for a moment. "If you want to try, if you think that you can trust me, I'll be waiting upstairs."

It was the longest half hour of her life. She paced the floor; she felt like running away. Standing in the center of the room, she nervously fondled the gown Thelma had given her. What if he didn't come? More agonizing, what if he did come, and it didn't work out? She'd told him she was willing to take that chance, but the odds were awfully high. She would lose more than her pride. When the door opened, she jumped a foot. Her heart began to pound with trepidation.

"Hello, Travis." It was the hardest thing she'd ever done, to walk toward him without wavering. "I think I forgot to say welcome home."

She stopped just in front of him and put her arms around his neck. For a moment, she thought he might pull away, but his lips met hers softly, tenderly. She arched against him and buried her hands in his thick hair, begging him with her body to love her.

With a harsh intake of breath, Travis clutched her to his hard length. "Oh, God, Reanna, don't do this if you don't mean it."

"I've never meant anything more," she murmured, reluctant to allow his lips to leave hers.

"I want you. I've wanted you for so long."

"I know, I've wanted you, too."

Further words weren't necessary. Travis gathered her in his arms and placed her tenderly on the bed. With infinite slowness, he removed the gown from her body, kissing every inch of flesh he exposed. A fire started in her loins and spread through her body like a raging tempest. Flames licked and smoldered, increasing in intensity, until at last their bodies were joined in the ages-old movement of love. With a boldness that surprised even her, Reanna met his every caress with one of her own, making love to him with a desperate fervor. Afterward, wrapped in a golden glow of fulfillment, she nestled in his arms. Travis kissed her tenderly.

"Did I ever tell you that you remind me of John Wayne?" she asked, running her fingers over his forehead to sweep back the lock of dark hair that had fallen over his brow.

"Once, long ago," he murmured back. "Although I never understood why."

"You're a hero," she explained. "*My* hero."

"That's quite an image to maintain." Frowning, he looked down at her. "What brought that up?"

"The nightgown with strawberries."

He laughed. "I couldn't resist. Did I ever tell you how much I detest your flannel gowns?"

"Once, long ago," she murmured, boldly tracing her fingers down his chest and along the darkened path of hair that disappeared into the sheet. "I promise to never wear them again, particularly my 'Christian Dior.'"

Travis smiled and lowered the covers, trailing his hands along her heated skin. "Maybe you can model it once in a while, just to give me the pleasure of removing it."

She lifted her face to his. All she could think of was his naked flesh pressed to hers with hard need. "I love you, Travis."

"Oh, God, Reanna," he murmured as his lips claimed hers again, "I love you, too, so damn much it scares me."

CHAPTER TEN

FOR THREE DAYS Reanna felt as though she were living in heaven. Her marriage was tremendously happy, her father had come to Martin Oaks, quickly recuperating, and Scimitar seemed to be in peak form. Without a single reservation, she left with Travis for the Hopeful. They took a plane again, traveling with the colt and with David, who kept glancing at them and shaking his head in bewilderment. No wonder, for they were behaving like a couple of teenagers, constantly touching, kissing, smiling at each other.

"Doesn't it ever get tiresome?" Travis's brother asked. "You've been married a couple months now."

Even Andy vocalized his disgust at their "mushy" behavior. "Gee whiz," he said, "I liked it better when you guys argued."

Reanna hadn't realized until then how astute their son was. Perhaps they had fooled the rest of the family, but obviously Andy had been aware of the undercurrents.

Mr. Martin was as happy as Reanna now that he had a crony to banter with. He would sit with her father for hours, trading insults and arguing about the merits of Kentucky-bred horses. Les Williamson would stubbornly insist that the birthplace of a Thoroughbred had nothing to do with success. To support their claims, they would each list a number of champions. Reanna wasn't certain if birthplace had anything to do with winning races, but she *was* certain Scimitar was destined for greatness. The big gray horse had finally settled down, and his speed was dizzying. She knew without a doubt that, this time, he would grace the winner's circle.

Nevertheless, her heart pounded with trepidation when the starting gate sprang open. There were ten other Thoroughbreds, all tough competitors, pounding down the turf with Iron Scimitar. There was a tense moment while the colt seemed to lug in at the rail; then, as if he was tired of the entire business of running with a crowd, he stretched out and romped home as though he were alone on the track.

The crowd gasped, and a few who had bet the long shot cheered and roared. Reanna was delirious. She jumped up and down, hugging Travis and screaming her delight. Her husband laughed, his gray eyes sparkling with love. "Let's get to the winner's circle," he said, guiding her through the crowd.

Scimitar was already there, but giving his jockey a bad time. The press of the reporters and the noise made him snort and prance. Without a qualm Reanna hugged him. Still stomping with displeasure, the colt nudged her with his head, expecting his usual treat. When she slipped him some raisins, a nearby reporter clicked a picture. Within moments, Scimitar became the darling of the press, his bad habits heralded as the sign of a winner.

"He's smitten with my wife," Travis explained to the sportswriters, laughing as the horse ate from her hand.

"Aren't you afraid he'll get cramps from the sugar?"

"It hasn't bothered him yet. You know, we all have a weakness, horses included. Scimitar's happens to be a soft voice and a bit of sweet."

Reanna smiled at him. She knew Travis wasn't referring just to Iron Scimitar.

Exactly one month later, as they celebrated their anniversary, Travis slipped her wedding band back on her finger.

"For all the right reasons, Reanna," he murmured. "In love and trust and belief in one another." Still holding her hand in his, he placed a thick envelope on the table. "I doubt if this will compensate for those weeks of mistrust, but I wanted to give you our premarital agreement. From this moment on, it's null and void. I love you, Reanna. Whatever I have is yours."

She looked up at him, forgetting the restaurant, the candlelight, the expensive meal. How desperately she loved him. "Let's go home, Travis."

They went home and made love for endless hours. Reanna had never felt so complete. Later, as Travis watched, she burned the document in the fireplace. To her, the flames that destroyed the papers became a symbol, a new beginning. Turning to her husband, she smiled and dropped her silky nightdress to the floor.

She suspected the baby was conceived that night. Or at least she liked to believe that their love and newfound trust had produced a child. For weeks, Reanna kept the secret to herself, reveling in the life that was growing within her body.

Travis showered her with gifts—new dresses, a sapphire ring, pearl earrings to match her necklace. There was so much that she couldn't have worn it all, particularly the nightgowns. He had a penchant for green, she discovered, and plunging necklines. She teased him that she would freeze to death if she wore any of the gowns he gave her.

They spent most of their time together. After working with the Thoroughbreds, afternoons they would ride the trails, Reanna on the dappled gray mare and Travis on Excalibur. Together they explored a small lake that sat nestled deep in the wooded area to the north of the estate. As a child, Travis had snuck off to swim in the secluded, frigid waters. Now they swam together and made love beneath the trees while the horses grazed nearby.

The days grew shorter and colder as September and October passed. Both children were settled in school. Jenny didn't need a tutor now that she was back in the classroom, but Reanna started working with her again to help the child accept the changes in all their lives. Jonathan was dating, and Jenny was having a hard time reconciling herself to a new mother figure. Reanna was glad Andy had accepted Travis so easily, and although it was good to see Jonathan interested in something other than his art, she felt compassion for his daughter's anxieties.

Reanna also spent a great deal of time with her father. Toward the end of October, he was released from the doctor. It saddened her to realize that Les was going to leave Martin Oaks. She would miss him, but at least they had reached a new understanding, and mutual forgiveness. Now he had Bold Intruder to train. Jokingly, he told her he'd see her at the Derby, for Iron Scimitar had become the shining star on the horizon. The gray horse kept winning, increasing his margin each time. The excitement of it was like all the holidays rolled into one. If he continued to run so well, the colt was clearly a contender for the Triple Crown the following year. In other major races, even without Les Williamson, Bold Commander was winning. Newspapers compared the two horses daily, making a match between them seem the event of the decade. Reanna read the releases with an indulgent smile. To her, it didn't matter which horse would win. They were both champions.

It was mid-November before she decided she should see a physician for a prenatal checkup. It hadn't occurred to her to confirm her pregnancy. She'd carried a child once before and was vividly aware of all the body changes and of the dietary requirements. But the school had notified her that Andy needed a blood test and a few booster shots. Not knowing any other doctor without going to the other side of the city, Reanna called Tom Marshall, the physician who had conducted the paternity tests on Andy. He would have a hemoglobin and hematocrit on record for her son and would probably give her the name of a nearby obstetrician.

Although his office was a shambles, Dr. Marshall was quite willing to verify what Reanna already knew before he referred her to another doctor.

"Is Charles rooting for another grandson? It seems to be all he ever talks about." The doctor was tall and fatherly. Reanna felt an immediate rapport with him.

"Mr. Martin doesn't know yet, and neither does Travis. I wanted to confirm my pregnancy before I tell the family."

"Well, this should do it," Dr. Marshall said as he drew a vial of blood. "I want you to see Dr. Samuels as soon as possible, and I'll give you the name of a pediatrician for Andy's physical, but I'll run a hematocrit on him to satisfy the school district in case you run into any scheduling problems. We'll just do a fingerstick."

"Andy will be delighted about that."

"Yes, he was rather vocal the last time I saw him."

Reanna laughed, grateful that Dr. Marshall didn't mention the paternity tests. Perhaps her pregnancy made him realize all was well at the Martin household. "He behaved terribly. When will I get the results?"

"Later today. You can call Marion this afternoon." He glanced around the office with a wry grin. "That is, if she can find it. Things are awfully confused around here. I hadn't realized how smoothly Sylvia ran things until she left for her honeymoon."

"Problems with the office help?"

"You don't appreciate the little details until they aren't done properly," he said, shaking his head. "If Sylvia doesn't get back soon I'm going to call out the National Guard to search for her."

Remembering the last time, Andy fussed again at having his blood drawn, but the lollipop the doctor handed him quickly squelched the tears. Reanna dropped him back off at school and drove home. She paced by the telephone for several hours before she dialed back.

Marion was in a tither, but she finally found Reanna's results. "Oh yes, it says here that the test is positive. Human chorionic gonadotrophin. What do you suppose that is?"

"It's a hormone, and it means I'm pregnant," Reanna said, laughing.

"Oh. Congratulations. Now let me see. You had something done on a little boy, too, didn't you?"

"Yes, a hematocrit."

"Humm, well, it doesn't say positive or negative so I guess it's all right. There's just a couple of numbers here."

"I'm sure it's fine, too," Reanna said. "Andy's healthy."

"I'll check with Dr. Marshall and call you if there's a problem."

"Thank you." Reanna smiled as she hung up the telephone. Efficiency wasn't Marion's strong point. Dr. Marshall was going to have to call out the army sooner than he expected. She took a vitamin and bounded upstairs, plans tumbling about in her head. It was going to be so much fun decorating a nursery. And she had to tell Travis, but she wanted to surprise him. Perhaps she could give him a diaper pin. She would wrap it as a present and make reservations for dinner. She wanted the moment to be special.

"Thelma," she called, pausing at the door to her old room. It would be a perfect nursery. It was large and airy, and the windows that faced the south would give the baby plenty of sunshine. She would sew curtains in hues of yellow and green and repaper with those clowns she had no-

ticed at the store last week. And she would need new furniture, a crib in white, perhaps, and a lamp that played
music. But first she had to clear out some of the things they
had stored in the closets. The room had become a catchall.
There were old magazines that had accumulated and boxes
of junk.

"Thelma, I want to clean out this room."

"Today? It's nearly dinnertime."

"Yes, right now." Reanna could barely contain her joy.
She grinned at the housekeeper. "I want to call the painters
right away, and tomorrow I'm going shopping for fabric. Is
there a sewing machine in the house?"

"A sewing machine? What on earth do you want a sewing machine for? If it's mending you want done, I can take
the things to the cleaners."

"I want to make some curtains."

"Curtains?" Thelma repeated, her tone curious.

"Never mind." Reanna smiled. "Let's get started."

She hadn't realized how late they had worked until she
heard Travis calling for her.

"Reanna?" His footsteps on the stairs made her heart
surge with joy. She wanted to blurt out the news, but managed to contain herself. She would surprise him, as she had
planned.

"Up here," she shouted, standing to relieve the cramps
in her legs. She had sat cross-legged for hours.

"What in the world?" Travis paused by the door. There
were stacks and stacks of garbage to be taken out and several bags of items she intended to give to charity.

"That's what I said," Thelma interjected.

Reanna handed the housekeeper a stack of magazines.
"Here, burn these. There's no reason to keep them."

"No reason at all," Thelma agreed, bustling from the
room. "Aside from the fact that we all want to eat tonight."

"I missed you this afternoon," Travis said, looking

around the room. "I guess I've been thrown over for a vacuum cleaner. I knew it was too good to last."

She grinned. "Just call me Suzy Homemaker."

"Well, Suzy—" He rubbed a spot on her cheek and kissed her lightly. "You're dirty."

Reanna laughed joyfully and snuggled in his arms, pressing provocatively against him. "Want to shower together? You could make certain I get clean."

"How much time do we have before dinner?" he whispered huskily, one hand reaching to caress her breast. "You're awfully filthy. It will take me ages to wash everything."

"We could skip the meal," she suggested, her eyes sparkling mischievously. "Strictly in the interest of hygiene, of course."

"Reanna"—his tone grew serious—"have I told you how very much I love you?"

"Yes," she murmured, leaning up for his kiss.

They were lost in the heady sensation of love as Travis's lips claimed hers. The telephone ringing produced a low groan from deep in his throat. "Do you suppose Thelma will answer it?"

"No." Reanna sighed, too. "I think she's busy with dinner." She kissed him again. "How about your father?"

"He's at the gallery with Jonathan."

"David?"

"At the stables cooling out Scimitar. I'd better answer." The persistent ringing hadn't stopped. "I'm expecting a call from Drew Mason."

She sniffled injuriously, "Always breeding horses, aren't you? Now *I've* been thrown over for a comely mare." Laughing, she pulled away. "And just when I had a surprise for you."

"Surprise?" He pulled her back into his arms. "What surprise?"

"It's a secret," she said smugly. "All I can say is that you're going to be quite shocked, Mr. Travis Martin."

He stared down at her with a puzzled grin. "That's not fair, Reanna, you can't leave me wondering."

"Yes, I can." When he kissed her again, she sighed. "Well, maybe I can be bribed."

"I thought so," he murmured, his lips nibbling a tempestuous trail along her neck. "How much?"

"Plenty."

"I've already paid plenty." He slid her buttons open and planted tiny kisses over her breasts.

"True, but I want more," she said, arching against him. Every nerve cell in her body was clamoring with arousal. She could hardly speak. "I want everything I can get."

"You're a scheming wench, Reanna Williamson Martin, as well as a temptress, but I have to answer that call." The shrilling telephone echoed through the house. "I'll catch you later with my payment."

"I'm holding out for high stakes," she teased. "Better bring along your fortune."

"It's a good thing I'm wealthy," he groaned. With a final, lingering kiss, he clambered down the steps.

Reanna smiled and went back to cleaning the room, content in their glorious love. That they could joke about bribery was a real step forward in their relationship. She could remember when their conversations regarding that subject were cruel accusations. After straightening up a bit, she went to check on Thelma. Since the housekeeper had been upstairs most of the afternoon, she owed her some help with dinner. But Thelma wasn't in the kitchen. Fully intending to sneak away for a shower, Reanna started back upstairs. At the study, she paused. Perhaps Travis could join her, after all.

"Travis," she called, but he was nowhere in sight. She glanced around the room, then remembered that she had neglected to answer the letter from her father. She'd put it in the drawer. Now she had some special news to impart. She went to the desk to retrieve it when Travis walked into the room, closing the door behind him. His face was totally ashen, and his lips were set in a grim line.

"Travis, is something wrong?" she asked.

"Wrong? Whatever could be wrong?" His glance at her was cold and angry as he strode to the sideboard and poured a glass of Scotch, neat. "Would you care to join me?"

Puzzled, Reanna frowned at him. Clearly something was amiss. "You know I don't drink."

"Ah, yes, I forgot." He drank the Scotch quickly and poured another glass. As he turned to her, a cynical smile twisted his lips. "It seems there are a lot of things I've forgotten about you, Reanna."

"What do you mean by that?" A knot of foreboding tightened in her abdomen. This abrupt turnabout confused her. Moments ago, they'd been lovers, and now the man facing her was a cold, hard stranger.

"What do I mean by that?" Angrily, he tossed off the second glass of Scotch. "Why, nothing. Nothing special, just how clever you are, and how detailed your little plan was. I underestimated you, Reanna—but then, I've underestimated you since the day you came here. Just how high were those stakes you were holding out for?"

Reanna was more confused than ever. What on earth had happened to change his attitude so drastically? "Travis, what are you talking about?"

"I'm talking about coincidences, Reanna. I'm talking about answering the phone and looking in a desk and discovering that where money is concerned, love flies out the window. Did you say you had a surprise for me? Well, I have a surprise for you, too. The scheme is over. I know the truth."

She hesitated for a moment. It was his tone that disturbed her. He sounded like a man who had been cruelly tricked, and he was more furious than she'd ever seen him before. "Travis, you're not making sense. Tell me what's happened."

"I think you can answer that better than I can. You tell me, Reanna, was it a coincidence that you suddenly wanted our marriage to work the day Andy's adoption became final? Was it a coincidence that you offered me your body the day I asked for a divorce?"

"Andy's adoption?" That was months ago—why was he bringing it up now? She stared at him blankly.

"You didn't have the money yet, did you? I hadn't given you anything, so you bargained with the only thing that you knew would keep us together. Do you know how desirable your body is, Reanna?" As he spoke, Travis strolled to the desk, his smile twisting deeper, wounding her more than his words. "Did you know how much I wanted you? You'd counted on that desire, hadn't you? How does it feel to sell yourself for cash?"

"Travis, I don't understand—"

"Cut the act, Reanna!" he interrupted. "You warned me, over and over. For months, you reminded me how devious you could be. Too bad I didn't heed your warnings. Too bad I didn't listen to your innuendoes. You were telling me even as we made love, even as we kissed a few moments ago. Have you enjoyed the charade? I hope my performance was up to par. Although my bank account was all you were interested in, I'd hate to think I disappointed you in the bedroom."

"Travis, please tell me who was on the phone." Desperation and confusion made her voice waver. "What did Drew Mason say to you that was so upsetting?"

"I didn't talk to Drew, Reanna. That was Dr. Marshall's office calling."

"Dr. Marshall?" It came out as an astonished whisper. Everything was happening so quickly it was difficult to assimilate.

Travis tilted his glass to her in a mock toast. "Yes, Dr. Marshall. It seems, my love, that there's been an error in the laboratory tests. Was that your surprise? When did you intend to tell me, tonight? Tomorrow? Or perhaps next week, after you'd gotten more money?"

It was as though the room had been thrust into total silence. Reanna felt herself turn pale. She sat in the nearest chair and touched her forehead with trembling hands. It wasn't true. There couldn't be an error! She was pregnant. She knew it as certainly as she was breathing.

"As you predicted, I did find it rather astonishing," he went on cruelly. "I was almost as amazed as you are, although for entirely different reasons. You had the advantage of knowing the truth, didn't you, love? In fact, you told me the night I proposed our preposterous arrangement that the tests could be erroneous. I must admit, you have my admiration. How did you accomplish it, Reanna? How did you convince a doctor to go along with you? Did you promise him half the money? In that case, I'm surprised you'd settle for a hundred thousand. As I recall, the price was half a million."

Reanna glanced up at him, relief that nothing was wrong with her unborn child immediately replaced by concern for her son. "The error—it—it was Andy?"

"Yes, the error was with Andy." He enunciated each word carefully, obviously conscious that his speech had become slurred with drink as he leaned over to stand face-to-face with her. "I guess you didn't count on a new receptionist. She was a little disorganized, but she was most anxious to notify me that Andy's results were incorrect." His laugh was a harsh, bitter sound. "She suggested that we could repeat the test at our earliest convenience."

It couldn't be. It wasn't possible. Andy was healthy. There had to be a mistake. Then she realized just what Travis was saying. He had assumed the receptionist was referring to the paternity tests! She clenched her hands tight to keep them from trembling. "Travis, you're wrong. You've misunderstood—"

"Wrong?" He practically pounced on her, his knuckles white where they clutched either side of her chair. "You're damned right I've been wrong. I've been a first-class fool, taken in by a soft voice and a voluptuous body. I happened to catch Thelma before she burned those magazines, Reanna. Did you think you could destroy them before I discovered that they chronicled the Martin Oaks rise to fame and fortune?"

"Travis, please listen to me," she cried. "I can explain."

"I'll just bet you can explain! God, Reanna, don't you ever quit pretending?" Pain had darkened his eyes to the color of molten lead, and his voice vibrated with raw emotion. "I know Andy is not my son. I know beyond a doubt that you came here with full knowledge of who I was, and if I needed further proof of your deception, I found the damned bankbook!" He tossed a small white deposit record on her lap and turned abruptly away, as though he couldn't bear to look at her. "Isn't that what you were searching for in the desk? You should be more careful with things that are so revealing."

Slowly, she opened the bankbook. There was a single deposit of one hundred thousand dollars. Where had it come from? Reanna stared at it for several long moments, not knowing what to say.

"The date of the deposit was the day after I gave you back our premarital agreement. Do you remember, Reanna? You made such a ceremony of burning those papers. A new beginning, I believe you said, a sign of trust and love." He laughed harshly. "Your affection is rather costly, darling."

Reanna sat in the chair, stunned. The evidence against her was overwhelming, but she still wanted him to believe in her. After what they'd shared these past months, his mistrust hurt more than anything. "I didn't make that deposit, Travis. That bank account isn't mine."

"How can you sit here and deny it, Reanna? It's right there in black and white. And the Martin Oaks account, which I might add, lists you as being able to sign checks, is missing one hundred thousand dollars."

Confused as to how all this could have happened, Reanna didn't bother to deny his accusation a second time. She stared down at her hands, paralyzed by indecision. What should she do? Should she leave? Should she defend herself? If the most innocuous misunderstanding could trigger his mistrust, it seemed useless to continue to protest her innocence.

There was a long silence while he stared at her. Then, sighing wearily, he raked a hand through his hair. "I don't really care about the bank account, not anymore. You're welcome to the money. I'd have given it to you, if you'd asked. I'd have given anything to you, Reanna."

Why couldn't she say it? Of all the gifts he could give her, there was only one thing she wanted: his trust. Without faith, there was nothing left to build on; without that one quality, their marriage was as empty and meaningless as the day they had taken their vows.

Travis crossed the room and placed his glass on the bar. There was a dreadful finality to his gesture. "Just once," he said, pausing and turning to her, "I'd like to hear the truth from you. Who is Andy's father? I think I have a right to know."

There was one chance left. Would he—could he—believe her? Could he give her that gift? She raised her eyes and met his gaze, appealing for his trust. "You're Andy's father."

"Don't you ever stop lying?" he asked quietly. "Reanna, there's nothing left to gain."

Tears formed in her eyes, but she choked them back. At that moment, she knew that her marriage was over—if it had indeed ever begun. What they had shared these past few months had been a fool's paradise, a Cinderella dream as insubstantial as wishful thinking. The odds were against them, and the stakes were too high. Agony formed a sharp ache in her heart.

"You're right, Travis," she said softly, "but not about gaining. There's nothing left to believe in." She held herself stiffly erect and turned from him. "I'll leave as soon as I can pack."

She was halfway out the door when Travis caught up with her and jerked her back. She gasped as he twisted her against his length.

"Just where the hell do you think you're going?" If she'd thought he was angry before, there was no comparison to the furious glints in his eyes now. And his hands clasped her wrist painfully. Yet his bitter wrath didn't frighten her. Cloaked in anguish, she was beyond fear.

"I'm leaving," she said calmly. "I should have gone the day you came home. Unfortunately, I stayed. I'll file for divorce as soon as possible."

"I've got news for you, lady, you're not going anywhere." The words seemed ripped from the depths of his soul, and there were taut, white lines around his mouth. "There won't be a divorce, either. You're my wife, and whether or not he's my child, I've adopted Andy and I love him. You won't take him away from here."

"What's the use, Travis? You don't trust me. You don't believe me. There's no reason for me to stay."

"That's where you're wrong, Reanna. For one hundred

thousand dollars, you owe me several more nights of passion. I intend to collect."

Suddenly, he was pressing her to his body and kissing her, his mouth harsh and rough. Whether it was from love and hope for the future, or for what might have been, Reanna moaned and arched against him, responding to the passion that flared between them. Clutching her tightly, he felt a hoarse cry escape from his throat, a signal of surrender, of desire.

Just as quickly, he thrust her away. Self-loathing filled his expression. "God help me, I still want you. No matter what you've done, I'll always want you!"

Turning on his heel, he headed for the door.

"Travis, wait!" she called, wondering why she was punishing herself in this manner. What she was about to confess was stupid, but some crazy hope of salvaging her marriage drove her to blurt out the words. "Travis, I'm pregnant."

She could hear the clock ticking and the sound of his even breathing. Spring could have passed into fall and fall into summer. Finally, he laughed. "How convenient. You get pregnant easily, don't you? For godsake, Reanna, do you really expect me to believe that?"

She held her head high; the ache in her heart grew sharper. "Whether or not it's convenient, I'm pregnant with your child."

For a brief moment, he seemed to hesitate. Ambivalence, combined with despair and stark desire, crossed his features. Then, as though exorcising a demon, he turned from her and swung out the door. Moments later, she heard the car roar to life, and then the squeal of tires on pavement as he sped down the drive.

Reanna wasn't certain how long she stood there staring at the empty doorway. It could have been hours. All she could think of was that her marriage was over—irrevocably over—and it hurt so bad she wanted to die. She clenched her hands together until her nails dug into her palms, hoping that the physical pain would overcome the anguish in her heart.

Slowly, she started to walk from the study. There was no other choice but to leave. As much as she loved Travis, he would never believe her; he would never trust her. It had been wrong from the first. Wrong to marry him, even for the sake of her child. It was her own fault; she had no one to blame save herself. She should have known they couldn't sustain a relationship on mere passion. There had to be something more, something deeper that bonded two souls together.

"Reanna?" Mr. Martin was standing in the hallway, leaning on his cane, looking puzzled. "Aren't you and Travis coming in to dinner?"

She stared at him blankly. "Travis has gone out," she finally murmured. "I—I'm not very hungry."

"Has something happened?"

"Happened?" The world had come to an end. The universe had ceased to exist. The stars had fallen from the sky. "Excuse me. I—I think I'll take a short walk."

Without further explanation, she grabbed a heavy jacket, then went out the door and down the neatly trimmed path. The ground crunched from a light frost, but she hardly noticed. Several minutes later, she was surprised to find herself at the stables, for she'd had no consciousness of heading there.

Charlie was just as surprised to see her. The groom looked up from repairing a lead line. "Howdy, Miss Reanna. Did you come to see Scimitar?"

Why was he so cheerful? Then she realized that there was no way Charlie could know that her world had fallen apart. "Can you saddle Lady for me?"

"You going for a ride now, this late? Maybe you'd best

take Excalibur instead. That Lady girl, she gets spooked in the dark."

"She'll be fine, Charlie," Reanna said. All she wanted to do was say good-bye to the mare. Perhaps that had been her intention in coming to the stables.

"I don't know, Miss Reanna, she's awful skittish today, and she's been off her feed. I think it's her time." For as long as he lived, Charlie would be convinced that female horses were comparable to their human counterparts: moody and unpredictable.

"Please saddle her, Charlie."

Shrugging and shaking his head, the groom walked off into the barns. While she waited, Reanna strolled down the cement path until she reached Scimitar's stall. "Hi, boy," she called.

The horse snorted and immediately came to the half entrance, nudging her with his nose. Through teary eyes, Reanna petted him.

"You know Travis is counting on you," she whispered, burying her face in his long mane. "He won't say it; he's too proud, but you're his Cinderella dream, and you can beat the odds. You're as fast as the wind. I can't be here to watch you win, but wherever I'm at, I'll root for you."

Scimitar pawed impatiently at the hay-strewn floor, tossing his head up and down. When Reanna turned abruptly away, he whinnied after her, sticking his head out the door. Refusing to look back, Reanna mounted the mare and wheeled around toward the north pasture.

"Be careful," Charlie called. "Don't stay out long."

Reanna rode briskly, heading into the densely wooded path toward the lake. Lady was skittish and seemed to shy at every shadow, but Reanna didn't concentrate on the mare, and only occasionally tightened the reins. It took nearly an hour to reach the knoll overlooking the placid water. She sat on the mare simply staring into nothingness.

After several moments, she dismounted, tying the reins loosely onto a bush. Lady started to graze on the long bluegrass.

Pulling her jacket close, Reanna walked to the shore and sat down, trying to hold back the tears that brimmed at her eyelids. She had to think clearly, but this confrontation with memories was making it harder. All she could think of was the warm fall days and the many times they had made love here. How desperately she loved Travis, still. And how was she going to take Andy from the father he adored?

A flock of crows settled in a nearby tree, and Reanna studied them for several long minutes. It was near dusk, and they were ready to roost for the night. They clustered together, snuggling close in an ageless dependency on one another. Reanna sighed and looked out over the water, watching the ripples that marred the smooth surface rush to shore; perfect circles expanding in ever-widening sequence, unbroken by distance or debris. If only love were like that, an endless circle immutable by any force. But that elusive emotion was more like the water, smooth and placid one moment, rough and turbulent the next. Why did it hurt so badly? Why did she feel destroyed?

The answer was easy: precisely because she loved him. *Then why was she contemplating leaving?* Abruptly, the thought occurred to her: If she loved him, didn't it stand to reason that she should fight to keep him? True, he had thought the worst of her; he'd hurt her, but he'd thought he had overwhelming evidence, and he'd been devastated to think that Andy wasn't his son. He'd admitted loving the boy, after all. He loved her, too, otherwise why had he been so anguished? Before he had walked out of the study, he'd looked at her with utter despair.

In retrospect, it was all so clear. Travis loved her. He loved her so much it had destroyed him to think that all she wanted was his money. These past weeks, he'd proven over and over how much he cared. He'd showered her with gifts, with devotion. Why hadn't she insisted that he call Dr. Marshall back? Instead of defending herself, she'd sat in the chair and allowed Travis to believe that she had been scheming all these months. She had let him assume that the tests were erroneous. If she were to prove to him how the error was made, he would have to accept the truth.

Love *was* an endless circle. The problem was that she had forgotten the vital points that kept it constant: understanding and forgiveness. Stubbornness had nearly cost her a relationship with her father. Was she going to let that same pride destroy her marriage?

Knowing suddenly what she had to do, Reanna jumped up from the ground. Startled by her abrupt movement, the birds swooped from the trees in a flurry of screeches. Behind her, the mare reared and whinnied, pulling at the loose reins.

"Lady!" Reanna cried. The horse was gone so quickly all she could do was stare as if at a gray ghost disappearing in the night. As if she didn't have enough problems, now she would have to walk home in the cold.

Home. Yes, she was going home. She would confront Travis and make him listen to reason. She would prove that Andy was his son, and she wouldn't leave without a fight. If he wanted her to go, he would have to evict her. As darkness enclosed the wooded area, she shivered and started down the path toward the house.

CHAPTER ELEVEN

AN HOUR LATER, when she reached the path that led to the house, the estate was ablaze with lights. The stable area was lit, too, several horses stood saddled, and the entire staff seemed to be running back and forth, talking excitedly. Even Jonathan was out front, looking confused. Travis was standing beside his father and David, getting ready to mount Excalibur. She could pick out his tall form from among the others, and she knew without a doubt that something was wrong. It was unusual for the barns and horses to be disturbed. It had to be Lady. Somehow the mare had been injured. Perhaps she had stepped into a pothole and pulled up lame. Thank goodness the children would be sleeping at this time of night. At least they wouldn't be in the way.

"Travis!" Reanna called, running the rest of the distance. "What's happened? Is it one of the horses? Did something happen to Lady?"

He whirled around, his face pale. "Reanna! My God, are you all right?" He enfolded her in his arms before she could answer. The thick jacket scrunched up between them. "Oh, Lord, I thought you were hurt."

"I'm fine," she said breathlessly. He was holding her so tight she could hardly breathe.

"I came back. I came back and you were gone. Charlie said you'd gone out riding, and when Lady came in by herself I almost went crazy." He kept holding her and kissing her. "God, Reanna, I thought I lost you. I'm so sorry. Please forgive me."

They were standing in front of the entire family and the servants, but she didn't care. She was laughing and crying at the same time. She'd been right. He *did* love her. She tried to extricate herself from his arms. "Travis, we have to talk."

"Reanna, please give me another chance. Please don't leave. Lord, I'm so sorry." His grip became even tighter. "I won't let you leave here." Now he was angry. She could tell by the tone of his voice, but his anger didn't faze her because she suddenly knew it was born of vulnerability. He was afraid of losing her. "If I have to tie you up and kidnap you, I won't let you leave here."

"I don't intend to leave," she murmured against the strong wall of his chest. Contrary to what she would ordinarily have felt at a man's domination, she was thrilled to know that he wouldn't let her go. "But I want to explain things. I want to explain about Andy."

"Reanna, it doesn't matter. Nothing matters except that you're all right. I don't care who Andy's father is. I don't care about the bank account, and I don't care why you came here. I love you, and I thought I'd lost you. When I realized what I'd done to you, the awful things I said to you—and when that mare came in alone, I wanted to die."

Despite his assurances, she wanted to set things straight. "Travis, that bank account you found in the desk isn't mine. I know it has my name on it, but I don't know where the money came from. I don't know—"

"I told you, I don't care about the bank account." They were both talking at once.

"Listen, both of you. Reanna, that bank account belongs to you."

They both heard Mr. Martin. The old man had hobbled toward them, and his words rang clear. Still holding her,

Travis turned to his father. Reanna felt her heart lurch. There was such overwhelming evidence against her already. Could she fight something else?

"Every penny in that bank account is yours. I know, because I put it there. Your father is a stubborn man, Reanna," Mr. Martin continued after a moment. "Les insisted on paying us back for his hospital bills. We worked out a deal. He gave me the only thing he had in this world, his interest in Bold Commander. I thought the horse was worth more than the few thousand dollars we loaned Les, and so I opened a bank account in your name for the rest of the money. I didn't tell either of you, because I thought one day, when he had the ready cash, I'd give it all back to Les. Commander may not be Kentucky-bred, but he's a winner."

"You didn't tell us?" Travis repeated. "One hundred thousand dollars, and you didn't tell us? Do you have any idea what problems you and Les have caused with your little deal?"

"I'm beginning to realize," the old man said, his face reddening. "It must be my arthritis. It's gone to my brain."

Travis started to speak, but Reanna waved him silent. "Thank you," she said, going to his father and kissing him on the cheek. He was a proud southern gentleman, and what he'd done was, to him, a matter of honor. "Thank you for being so thoughtful and so honest."

Mr. Martin nodded, but he was glaring at Travis. "However, my senility hardly excuses you, Travis. I'm not hard of hearing, so I know *you* have some things to apologize for, too. Now before you mess things up entirely, you better get Reanna somewhere private to make amends."

"That's exactly what I had in mind." Travis laughed and swept her into his arms.

Except for their surroundings, the moment was so reminiscent of their wedding night that Reanna's face reddened when the bystanders all started to cheer. It didn't matter though, that they had a captive audience. When he kicked the door to their room closed and set her down, she turned to him and smiled. After removing her jacket, slowly, provocatively, she started to unbutton her blouse.

"I never did get that shower," she murmured. "And I have a new nightgown I wanted to show you."

"I hope it's green," Travis said, grinning. The barely checked passion in his eyes was exciting. Their gazes met and locked; then, folding her into his arms, he kissed her hungrily and pushed her toward the bathroom.

Reanna thought she was never going to get clean. True to his earlier prediction, he found spot after spot that required washing. As he kissed her turgid nipples and ran his hands over her slightly protruding abdomen, his voice was almost reverent. "You are pregnant, aren't you?"

"Yes," she murmured, melting against him.

"Oh, Reanna, I love you so much."

They made love in the shower, and again on the bed. Later, Travis insisted that she model her nightgown, but he took it off so quickly that she objected that he didn't even see it.

"You didn't even look!"

"Sure I did," he said, kissing her. "I told you it was green. It has little green vines."

She squirmed away. "This gown is fire-engine red! Travis, I'm beginning to think you're color-blind."

"It's not the nightgown I wanted to see." He recaptured her in his arms. "Besides, I like you naked."

"Even if I freeze to death? These Kentucky winters are cold."

One hand snaked over her thighs, and he laughed huskily. "Then let me light the fire."

He obviously wasn't talking about the fireplace. Molten flames spread through her body as he kissed her thoroughly. Each caress increased the feverish pitch until Reanna thought surely her bones had melted. All she could think of was his naked flesh next to hers. When at last their bodies joined in a joyous affirmation of love, a fiery glow of fulfillment nestled in the center of her being.

Afterward, lying in his arms, Reanna happened to notice a small produce carton on the dresser. It looked so out of place. "Travis, what in the world is that?" she asked curiously.

Travis followed her gaze. "That, my love, is a bit of magic. Strawberries." At her stunned expression, he started to explain. "I went out of here like a madman. When I realized what I had done, I hoped to make amends. I would have done anything to keep you, Reanna, but I didn't know if you'd listen. I said some pretty cruel things, so I stopped at the store before I came home. I hoped you'd remember that first night we met. Do you remember? You were drinking champagne punch."

"Yes, I remember." How could she have forgotten? She'd loved him even then.

"All I could think of was getting you to listen." He went to the dresser, picked up a bottle that was enclosed in a paper bag, and poured two glasses of champagne. Then he plopped a strawberry into each glass. "I had a hell of a time finding the damned things this time of year. Strawberries are out of season. I know you don't drink, and I think I know why, but how about just one toast?" He tipped his glass to her. "To us, to magic."

"Wait." She held the champagne in her hand. "Travis, I think we should talk. There are still some things that you should know."

"The only thing I have to know is that you love me and that you've forgiven me."

"Travis, in a marriage people understand and forgive. I didn't realize how important that was until today, but the truth is important, too. I want you to know that Andy is your child."

He stepped toward her. "Whether or not he's biologically mine doesn't matter. Andy is and will always be my son. I don't care. You don't need to explain."

"But *I* care," she said. "Travis, would you please listen to me? I've been trying to tell you that the error wasn't in the paternity tests. It was a hematocrit that was drawn today."

"You mean . . . ?"

For a moment he looked joyous, then his expression changed to a concerned frown. "Is something wrong with Andy?"

"No, the test is necessary for him to continue in school. It's a state law. Andy's healthy, and I'm certain the error is just something minor. If you noticed, Dr. Marshall's receptionist was terribly confused."

"Yes," he agreed, taking her into his arms. "I noticed. Reanna, I'm so sorry. I'm sorry for doubting you."

"You thought you had reason," she said. "I'm sorry for letting you believe the worst. I should have defended myself."

"I guess we both have a lot to learn." His kiss was so tender it brought tears to her eyes. "Maybe I need a trainer to keep me in line, like Scimitar."

"Travis," she said with animation, relieved at the excuse to change the subject before the apologies became too abject and maudlin, "what's going to happen when Scimitar and Bold Commander race against each other next year in the Derby? Which one do you think will win?"

"Aren't you thinking awfully far ahead? A lot can happen between then and now."

"I know, but it's going to be so exciting."

He shrugged. "Yes, the sportswriters are calling it the

match race of the decade, but either way, you'll be in the winner's circle."

"Maybe it will be a dead heat," she mused.

"That's a good solution, but it would be unusual," he said. "Did you know that Lynda's Pride was nominated for the Derby, too?"

She laughed. "Are you suggesting she might beat them both?"

"She's quite a filly."

"Would you be upset if Scimitar lost to her again?"

"As you said, she's awfully pretty. Scimitar would be showing his good taste. And besides, how could I be upset with him when I've lost my heart to a female of my own species?"

"He won't lose, Travis," she said. "I have faith."

"So do I." He enfolded her in his arms and looked down at her lovingly, one hand lightly caressing her rounded abdomen. "So do I, Reanna."

SECOND CHANCE AT LOVE

COMING NEXT MONTH

ALL THAT JAZZ #424
by Carole Buck

Jazz O'Leary doubts her blood's blue
enough for Ethan Wilding, but he takes her
troubled teenage protégés in stride and
reformed bad-girl Jazz into his arms
and heart, clearing her of complicity
in a computer scam, and even
decking an FBI agent!

IT STARTED WITH A KISS #425
by Kit Windham

Bridesmaid Henrietta Jones jumps out
of a bachelor-party cake into the arms of
best man Sam Marchand. Impulsively,
Sam gives her a grandstand kiss...
and the rest is chemistry!
Sam's con-man grandfather and Henrietta's
coterie of male admirers add humor.

Second Chance At Love

Be Sure to Read These New Releases!

ACCENT ON DESIRE #420
by Christa Merlin

Five-feet-and-feisty investigative reporter
Maggie Burton "kidnaps" a sexy stranger's
groceries—then learns he's her boss,
newspaper publisher Todd Andrews! Todd
wants Maggie off his paper and home
on his ranch; she uncovers a local scandal,
adding new drama to their love...

YOUNG AT HEART #421
by Jackie Leigh

Medical editor Rhetta Stanton falls
hard for dazzling heart surgeon "Mac"
McHale. He savors feeling young at
heart in Rhetta's embrace, but as a widower
he knows the pain of loving and losing.
The poignant theme is lightened by the
author's famed humor and gift for banter.

Order on opposite page

SECOND CHANCE AT LOVE

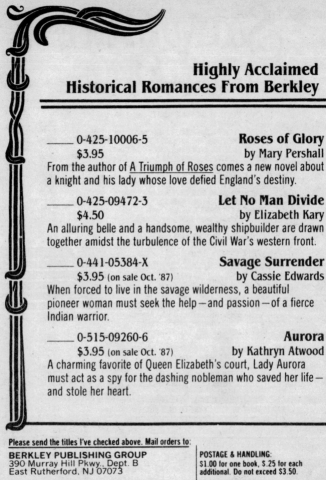